LIFE &
DEATH
DECISIONS
—— IN THE ——
C-SUITE

HOW THE U.S. INSURANCE SYSTEM
PUTS YOUR EMPLOYEES' LIVES
AND HEALTH AT SERIOUS RISK ...

AND HOW YOU CAN FIX IT

HIGH
ROI
PRESS

Published by High ROI Press

ISBN (ebook):   978-0-9882823-7-7
ISBN (paperback): 978-0-9882823-8-4
ISBN (hardcover): 978-0-9882823-9-1

*This book is dedicated to those business leaders
and executives who understand the critical
importance of their decisions and who want to
do all they can to create the best possible outcomes
for their organization and their employees.*

Contents

Preface

by Deborah Ault
President, Ault International Medical Management

L ET ME TELL YOU A SCARY STORY.
No, this isn't a horror novel. Unfortunately, this exact TRUE
story plays out day after day after day in our US healthcare system
and in the lives of the people we love, admire, adore, and serve.

Mr. A was an active, well known and respected sixty-six-year-
old member of his community when I first came to know him. He
was actually the mayor of his town, and that town provided him
with healthcare coverage through a self-funded employer sponsored
health plan. That's how I came to know him — my firm was hired
by his employer to perform the medical management services associated with his health plan administration. In short, they hired us
to ensure that their beloved employees (and their family members)
were getting the right care, at the right time, in the right place, for
the right price. Granted, if you get the right patient into the right
care, at the right time, in the right place, the vast majority of the

time the right price is the NATURAL consequence, but let's reserve that discussion for another day.

Unfortunately, Mr. A had been diagnosed with lung cancer shortly before my firm was engaged to assist him. Before we got to know him, he and his physicians had already decided on a treatment plan. Nonetheless, we developed a rapport with him and were working with him and his treatment team to help them navigate the two most cumbersome ecosystems in the universe — the health delivery system and the health plan system.

As part of our responsibilities toward ensuring right care, we perform the precertification of certain medical procedures and services — including chemotherapy. Such was our responsibility in this case — to determine the medical necessity and appropriateness of a particular chemotherapy request as a condition of coverage under the health plan.

We gathered all the information pertaining to the proposed chemotherapy regimen and all the pertinent clinical information pertaining to the patient. As is our standard process with chemotherapy requests, we had a board-certified and highly qualified and credentialed physician review the patient's clinical situation and the proposed chemotherapy regimen. We asked that specialist physician a number of questions pertaining to this case (13 questions to be exact) centered around the safety and efficacy of the proposed treatment, along with plan requirement considerations. We even asked our specialist physician to connect with the patient's treating physician by phone to complete a peer-to-peer conversation to ensure that we had a full understanding of the patient's situation and the rationale for this particular proposed treatment plan.

Upon review of the case, our specialist physician had some serious concerns. Namely, the patient's liver function. Why, you might ask, does one care about liver function when the case involved is lung cancer? Well, because the proposed chemotherapy is metabolized primarily through the liver, and without proper liver function, the danger in using this chemotherapy is greatly increased.

Our physician called the ordering/treating physician to explore why this particular chemotherapy was going to be administered given that recent liver function tests had not been performed, and the treating physician responded, "Genomic testing was used to choose the chemotherapy regimen". And, while genomic testing is super cool, it should not be used in isolation.

Our decision on the chemotherapy request was a denial. We deemed it experimental/investigational and expressed serious concerns about the risks given the absence of liver function testing.

The plan sponsor (the patient's employer) was displeased with this denial. As a result, they consulted with a different medical management vendor. That medical management vendor's NURSE (not a PHYSICIAN, a NURSE) told them that if she were presented with this case and asked to make a precertification decision she would CERTIFY or AUTHORIZE the request. She cited NCCN as her rationale. (It is worth noting that our PHYSICIAN had also considered NCCN, but the category of evidence in NCCN was such that this case still warranted a denial.) She did not address liver function at all in her "recommendation" or "decision".

As a result, the plan sponsor decided to override our denial and certify the request. That override empowered the provider and the chemotherapy was administered (isn't it interesting that the healthcare providers were NOT willing to administer the chemotherapy without knowing they would be paid for it? But that's a whole other book…).

Twelve days after the (now approved for coverage under his health plan) chemotherapy was administered, the patient passed away. The news article about his passing spoke in a very roundabout way about his death being related to chemotherapy complications.

I was heartbroken and livid at the same time.

Would this patient have died "no matter what"? Possibly. We all die. Would he have gotten a few extra hours, days, weeks with his family and beloved community if they had NOT given that particular chemotherapy? There's no way to know for sure, but many clinicians involved in the case afterward said "YES". His life was actually shortened by the treatment.

As an employer sponsoring healthcare coverage for your employees and their families, YOU are making life and death decisions for those people EVERY DAY. The vendors you pick as a part of your health benefits are your responsibility, and they are representing YOU when they approve or deny the coverage of medical procedures and services.

As a benefits consultant, the vendors you recommend to your clients are serving these patients. Those vendors represent YOU when they approve or deny the coverage of medical procedures and services. Choose them wisely…because, as demonstrated in the situation above, not all vendors are motivated by the care and safety of the patient. Not all are clinically competent. Not all are financially savvy. Not all are adequately prepared and supported to fix what is broken in the American healthcare system today.

Think this is an isolated incident? Think again.

Mr. M lived fifty-one days after getting a chemo that we denied, because his broker said (at least the patient's wife says this is what the broker said), "I'll deal with the insurance, you just go get your chemo".

So, it's just chemo? Nope.

Mr. N insisted (against our advice,) on using a physician with a very low-quality score to have a PTCA (heart cath) procedure done at a facility we recommended against. We were not a fan of the chosen facility because they didn't have open heart capability. During the procedure one of his heart vessels was ruptured and he nearly died during transport to another facility to get emergency open heart surgery. He nearly died during the recovery from his open-heart surgery. Thankfully, he lived. (When he later decided to get a knee replacement surgery, he followed our advice and had a very uneventful surgery and smooth recovery.)

Mrs. M was approved for a robotic hysterectomy just days before our firm became a part of her health plan. We would NOT have approved use of a robot for her surgery had we been doing the precertification decision making. She exemplifies a healthcare horror story. You can hear her story, told by her, at: https://vimeo.com/533117992

Mr. J broke his ankle. His employer and broker pressured us to approve a surgery to address a traumatic fracture, despite the proposed surgeon having a very low-quality score. They didn't want the patient inconvenienced by a delay in approval so that a conversation about a potential change in surgeon could occur. "HURRY UP!" they cried. So we did. The procedure was necessary, so an authorization was issued. The patient got an infection that just might kill him. Mr. J, if he lives through his bout with Sepsis (infection in the blood), is very likely going to lose his foot and be crippled for life.

Mrs. M refused to consider changing surgeons because this surgeon (chosen before we became a part of her health plan) had done surgery on her other knee. His quality score was 7.1 (out of 100). This surgery didn't go so well as demonstrated by her more than $356,000 in medical bills, and the limp she still walks with today.

How many more of these horror stories will it take to convince you that _**you are making life and death decisions (whether you want to or not)**_ when you are involved in picking insurance and providing healthcare coverage to your employees? Because I can go on, and on, and on...

Mrs. J wanted an eye injection. It was denied, since it was an off-label use which resulted in it falling under the plan's definition of experimental/investigational. We tried to get the patient to seek the treatment through a clinical trial that was enrolling patients at the time. It was a "perfect match" for her, but she didn't want to stop seeing her physician — and he didn't want to give her (employer's checkbook) up as a patient. The plan, in their great wisdom, over-rode the denial and paid for the treatment. Now, a year later, the patient is blind in that eye. A predictable possible outcome of the treatment, and one that the patient did NOT have TO sign a form acknowledging as a potential risk of the treatment. If she had been in a clinical trial, she would have had to sign a form. I wonder how much she loves that doctor now?! And I wonder if his malpractice premiums will go up by more than the amount he made off of this employer sponsored health plan?

Ms. Q desperately wanted a robotic hysterectomy. Her physician had convinced her it was the best way to go. We tried to talk her out of it and provided her with every statistic and study we could get our hands on, but she wouldn't listen. She and her doctor decided to go ahead with the robotic procedure anyway. "We won't bill the insurance for the use of the robot" was the compromise her doctor made. You guessed it. They nicked her bowel during the surgery. She became septic and nearly died, spending WEEKS in the ICU on a ventilator. To this day she is getting therapy for the PTSD pre-cipitated by that surgery, and she's still pooping into a colostomy bag. The union representing this patient throws a royal fit TO THIS DAY every time we deny a robotic hysterectomy on one of their other members. They literally told me that, "Our job is to get our people what they want" — never mind the pain and suffering it's going to inflict on them or the financial devastation it's going to impose on EVERYONE in the plan.

Mr. S was eager to have an elective/non-emergency knee surgery. We "stalled" the authorization and demanded to talk to the patient, mainly because the surgeon he chose has a 10.7 (out of 100) quality score. We did our best to get him to go to a higher quality surgeon who, by the way, was even CLOSER to his home than the physician with the poor score. Mr. S refused because he didn't want to delay the surgery on this knee by another week or two (or even a month) since the pain had been "killing him" for two years. He insisted, so we went forward with the authorization. He had the surgery, and was then admitted emergently into the ICU of his local hospital with a limb threatening infection. He is lucky he didn't turn septic and die. He underwent three more surgeries and was bedridden for MONTHS — at some points having nothing (no bone and no metal device) connecting his upper leg to his lower leg, because the infected bone and device had to be removed. He lived, and after months of therapy learned to walk again.

SPEAKING OF LOSING LEGS — how about the patient who needed to have bowel surgery? What's the correlation between his bowel and leg? Well, follow me here: We strongly discouraged him from his chosen surgeon and pointed out that the hospital where his wife works, and where his health insurance was through, both had a higher quality surgeon who would do the surgery FOR FREE if he would change his surgeon and go to the home facility for the surgery. He refused, saying he and his wife were "too private" for him to have surgery where she works. Yeah, well, the surgery went so wrong that during the procedure they cut off the blood flow to his legs. He had to have a revolting surgery to slice open his leg from groin to ankle to try to prevent the swelling from cutting off circulation and killing his leg. That leg got gangrene and he was on the cusp of losing the leg. The "only hope" was hyperbaric oxygen treatment (think of those pictures of kids in giant "iron lungs" back in the day — that's essentially what this treatment is like — talk about miserable!). The problem was, that treatment was experimental/investigational. There was ZERO chance that his health plan was going to pay (one of their competitors) to deliver that treatment. BUT, if the patient wanted the treatment and would come back to his home facility, they would administer the treatment and not charge him for it. He relented, went to the home facility, got the treatment, and miraculously the leg was saved (although I doubt he is able to walk without pain and a limp). Thank goodness his need for extreme privacy didn't cause him to lose his leg... (trust me, nobody wanted to be all up in his business anyway...it's not like he was some George Clooney level celebrity...he was just a normal person for goodness sake!).

Now, you are probably wondering "Why would you write the negative? Aren't there enough GOOD stories to tell?" Well, yes. There are literally THOUSANDS of good stories, great outcomes, and even people who respond with, "THANK GOD YOU WERE THERE". But those stories are constantly being told. To be frank, we are battling a very, very serious pandemic of "I want the outcomes, but I'm not willing to polish up the brass cojones and deal with the price/noise/pain necessary to obtain those outcomes" amongst the decision makers involved in purchasing healthcare coverage/insurance.

We always seem to have a very LOW VOLUME but HIGH DECIBEL handful of cases going on, and it seems that too many employers and, quite frankly, the advisors who consult with them on their health plan, are losing sight of WHY what we are doing around RIGHT care, RIGHT time, RIGHT place, RIGHT price IS SO CRUCIAL.

Unfortunately, it only takes one (or two) "well-placed" or "well-loved" or "politically-influential" or "pain in the ass" people on the plan who want what they want, when they want it, because they believe they are entitled to it to create real, potentially catastrophic problems for themselves and the health plan. These individuals are

NOT armed with all the science and facts yet they bend the ear of the "right person" at the employer who is an expert at what THEY do but not at what they have hired US to do. That leader will then turn and run to the advisor who really does NOT want to be spending their time "defending" the decision or dealing with unhappy clients! The advisor then will often come to us frustrated or angry because we are doing not only what we are paid to do, but also doing what is in the best interest of the patient and health plan.

So, I ask you, dear reader. Where do **you** stand on this issue? Do you want to protect and serve every person within your sphere of influence? Are you willing to equip them with the tools, resources, and support necessary to make the best possible decisions when it comes to their health, the care they receive, and the providers they utilize to obtain that care?

If your answer is "YES" (or better yet — "OH HELL YES"), then please continue on and read the rest of this book.

Introduction:
"A Matter of Life and Death"

by Nelson Griswold
Chairman, NextGen Benefits Network

O<small>N A STAGE IN DALLAS,</small> in April of 2021, at the quarterly meeting of the exclusive NextGen Benefits Mastermind Partnership, Deb Ault stood in front of 80 elite healthcare benefits professionals and reminded them that, in the final analysis, their work with employee health plans is "a matter of life and death."

Deb Ault, RN, MBA, founded and runs Ault International Medical Management (AIMM), one of the premier medical utilization management firms in the U.S. Her firm is an essential part of a large majority of employer-sponsored health plans based on the new NextGen Benefits model for employer-sponsored healthcare plans.

With her emphatic statement that building and implementing employee health plans can be a life and death proposition, Deb not only galvanized the assembled advisers but inspired the title of this book. Her stirring words applied not only to healthcare advisers but also to business owners and company executives who make life and death decisions in the C-Suite…when choosing the health plan for their employees.

This book explains exactly how business leaders, despite their vocal denials, every year make a life and death decision that, currently, puts the life and health of their employees — and their families — at terrible risk. And the book explains just who is responsible for the current system that puts employees at such risk.

More important, the authors provide an alternative to the status quo healthcare system, an alternative that eliminates the risk and ensures high-quality healthcare with better outcomes for the company's employees and their family members.

This book will open the eyes of business owners and executives to the unnecessary risks to which they are subjecting their employees. Once these business leaders recognize that the current model presents an unacceptable level of risk, they will discover in this book a high-level overview of the NextGen Benefits alternative to the dangerous status quo.

The purpose of this book is not to transform owners and executives into experts on healthcare benefits; that's the job of their healthcare advisers and consultants. Rather, the book's purpose is to jolt owners and executives into an awareness of their responsibility to recognize and mitigate the risks to employees from their employer-sponsored healthcare plan.

We certainly don't expect owners and executives themselves to implement the strategies and techniques in this book to provide their employees with safe and high-quality healthcare. We do, however, expect right-thinking owners and executives to avail themselves of the experience and expertise of NextGen Benefits advisers and consultants to implement a healthcare plan that delivers superior medical outcomes.

Finally, these owners and executives should know that the reward for choosing a NextGen health plan is not just the higher-quality care for plan members, but a financial windfall for their company and the elimination of out-of-pocket expenses for the employees.

We hope that the promise of those rewards will serve to induce the reader to continue reading. Since every company makes this critical decision every year, this book will show owners and executives how to protect the life and health of their employees by making the *right* life and death decision in the C-Suite.

1

Life & Death Decisions in the C-Suite

by Nelson Griswold

B USINESS OWNERS, CEOS, AND CFOS will scoff at the idea that they make life and death decisions in their office or in the boardroom. While they acknowledge that they sometimes make difficult and painful decisions affecting their employees, these business leaders will argue that the choices they make never rise to the level of life and death decisions.

They're dead wrong. Every year, owners and executives make a major decision that puts the life and health of their employees at substantial risk, a risk that can prove fatal.

Here are the facts of the life and death decisions made in almost every American C-Suite and how these owners and executives can stop putting their employees at terrible risk…and how that decision can create a financial windfall for their company.

* * *

Brain tumor.

That's the terrifying diagnosis a friend of mine — I'll call him Dennis — shared with me recently.

A brain tumor.

Fortunately, Dennis has good health insurance and access to a highly regarded academic medical center.

Dennis' neurosurgeon — we'll call him Dr. Z — had excellent online scores on the subjective, "soft" quality rating websites, based on patient opinions. On a 1-5 scale, Dr. Z was rated a 5 on Healthgrades, a 4.9 on his health system website, and a 5 on Sharecare.

So Dennis felt confident in his medical team, but he knew a healthcare insider who offered to run Dennis' neurosurgeon through a data analytics platform that measures physicians' and hospitals' medical outcomes. Dennis seized the chance to get quality scores on his doctor because, after all, his choice of neurosurgeon very well could be a life and death decision.

Using doctor-reported outcomes data compiled by the federal Centers for Medicare and Medicaid Services (CMS), this industry-leading platform scores the quality of the physician's patient outcomes in a wide range of clinical categories. Most important, the data analytics platform employs highly sophisticated proprietary algorithms to adjust for risk and severity, ensuring statistically valid scoring. Nearly a thousand hospitals and healthcare systems utilize this particular platform for healthcare quality analytics.

Objective quality scores

Dennis' doctor ranked high on subjective patient scores, but what were the *objective* quality scores for this neurological surgeon at this nationally known health system, based on his own self-reported patient outcomes?[1]

In the key category rating his **neurological surgical outcomes**, Dr. Z scored an **8.4**, a respectable score…if the range was 0-10.

But these scores are on a 0-100 point scale, from Very Poor to Excellent. Dr. Z's 8.4 quality score rates him **Very Poor** for surgical outcomes.

In the related category rating **neurological care**, Dr. Z's score was a **17.1**, **Poor**, impacted most by an unacceptably high level of patient readmissions to the hospital.

Dr. Z's outcomes scores for his **surgical care** and **hospital care** were **9.7** and **9.3**, respectively, both **Very Poor**.

With these abysmal outcomes scores, it's clear that Dr. Z is a dangerously bad surgeon.

What patient with a brain tumor would choose a neurosurgeon with these quality outcomes? Isn't it safe to say that no patient would, who had this information?

"I spent a good 30 minutes rapidly going through the stages of grief on this," Dennis said. "Please take that the right way - the info is invaluable," he added.

Despite the impact of this information on him personally, Dennis recognized the bigger problem, "Another example of a lack of transparency in the medical world that may have horrible results."

The unacceptable reality in the U.S. healthcare system is that almost no patients *ever* know doctors' outcomes quality scores to make an educated decision on who will treat them.

If you are the patient, how do you feel about making what could be a life and death decision — choosing your doctor and your

---

1   Due to the proprietary nature of the outcomes quality data and the platform's restrictions on public usage of the data, the analytics platform must remain unnamed.

hospital — completely blind, without any insights into quality and safety other than the uneducated opinions of other patients?

If this is your valued employee, how do you feel knowing that your employees receive no objective information or guidance on the quality of healthcare providers and their outcomes?

If this is you or a family member, how do you feel knowing that you have no idea whether your doctor is exceptional… or exceptionally bad — and you'll get no help from your insurance company?

The insurance companies' dirty secret

Why did Dennis have to get his doctor's quality scores from a friend with access to this outcomes data? Why didn't Dennis' health insurance company provide him the quality scores? Full of extremely intelligent people and with billions in revenue, insurance carriers certainly have access to health provider quality scores.

So why is physician and hospital quality data so hidden and, for the patient, unavailable? In fact, patients don't even know quality data like this exists. Why?

The reason is that health insurance companies have a filthy secret when it comes to provider quality scores and patient outcomes and safety.

The health insurance companies, whose members pay them ridiculously well to ensure quality medical care, **cannot** share provider quality data with their members. Their provider network contracts with doctors and hospitals prohibit insurance companies from steering members away from bad providers and to high-quality providers.

These network contracts prevent the carriers from favoring or promoting one doctor or hospital in the network over another… *even when* one doctor is dangerous and another is a superb surgeon, even when one hospital has a high infection rate and another is clean and safe.

Providers over patients

Of course, it's important to understand that the insurance carriers have made a conscious decision not to disclose this potentially life-and-death information to their members, even knowing that it puts patients at risk of serious injury or even death. The insurance companies themselves wrote these network contracts that keep provider quality scores a secret from their own plan members.

Clearly, the insurance companies have decided it's more important to protect doctors and hospitals from their bad quality scores than to protect their members from dangerous doctors and unsafe hospitals.

The insurance company doesn't even use this important provider quality data to screen out physicians and facilities who pose a threat to their members.

Cancerous tumor on the pelvis

When Maureen Pacheco of Palm Beach, FL, needed spinal fusion surgery in 2016, general surgeon Ramon Vazquez was assigned to cut her open so the two spine surgeons could perform the fusion procedures.[2]

A Board-certified surgeon, Dr. Vazquez is a Harvard University graduate with a medical degree from New York's prestigious Albert Einstein College of Medicine, with top ratings on Google, Vitals, and U.S. News & World Report. All the evidence points to Dr. Vazquez being a great doctor.

After cutting open Ms. Pacheco, Dr. Vazquez noticed a mass on her pelvis. Believing it to be a cancerous tumor, he removed the mass in its entirety, without a biopsy or the patient's permission, then allowed the spinal procedure to continue.

---

2   Lindsey Bever, "A woman went to a hospital for back surgery — and left without one of her kidneys," Washington Post, November 2, 2018, https://www.washingtonpost.com/health/2018/11/02/woman-went-hospital-back-surgery-left-without-one-her-kidneys.

Following a successful spinal surgery, Ms. Pacheco woke up in recovery to an unexpected — and horrifying — outcome. She now had two fused vertebrae…and one kidney.

What Dr. Vazquez presumed to be a malignant tumor was, in fact, Ms. Pacheco's healthy left kidney, a "pelvic kidney" that had never moved up to its normal position in the upper abdomen. Dr. Vazquez later acknowledged that he never reviewed his patient's medical records before the surgery, which would have revealed the pelvic kidney.[3]

Yet, even after removing a patient's healthy kidney, settling the resulting malpractice suit, getting dismissed by the hospital where the surgery occurred, fighting off the state's efforts to revoke his medical license, and agreeing to pay a $3,000 fine, Dr. Vazquez remains a doctor in good standing in the Florida Blue (BlueCross BlueShield of Florida) provider network. His listing in the Florida Blue online physician directory offers no warning or any indication to the member that this is a doctor with poor patient outcomes and a recent case of gross negligence.[4]

Of course, a reasonable and generous person could view what happened to Ms. Pacheco simply as a terrible but well-intentioned mistake on the part of Dr. Vazquez. After all, until then he had a clean disciplinary file with the state Board of Medicine.[2]

If one were to check his surgical outcomes quality scores, however, one might discover scores that confirm Dr. Vazquez to be a bad surgeon.[5]

What is most concerning isn't that there are bad doctors like Ramon Vazquez. There always will be bad doctors and unsafe

---

3   Associated Press, "Surgeon fined $3K for removing kidney he thought was tumor," January 11, 2019, https://abcnews.go.com/US/wireStory/surgeon-fined-3k-removing-kidney-thought-tumor-60307980.
4   Florida Blue, "Find a Doctor," accessed November 2, 2021, https://providersearch.floridablue.com.
5   Again, usage restrictions and copyright laws prevent the use of any actual quality scores in this example.

hospitals, of course, but shouldn't we expect our health insurance company to protect us from them, and to guide us to the best providers?

Low-volume, high-risk hospitals

In hospitals, a high volume of any particular surgical procedure almost always equates to high quality. Most patients are unaware that the opposite is equally true, that low volume of a surgical procedure in a hospital equates to high risk for patients having the procedure at that hospital.

Patients undergoing high-risk surgeries are more likely to suffer complications, harm, or even death when the surgeon and/or hospital are inexperienced at that procedure. In one low-volume hospital, an analysis by *U.S. News & World Report* showed that patients were 24 times more likely to die from a knee replacement surgery than in the highest-volume facilities.[6]

This problem is extremely widespread. Fully 87.8 percent of hospitals perform open heart procedures too infrequently to ensure patient safety and high-quality medical outcomes. And 90.9 percent of hospitals similarly perform rectal cancer surgery too infrequently.[7]

The BUCAH (Blue Cross, UnitedHealthcare, Cigna, Aetna, Humana) insurance companies know which hospitals perform a sufficiently high volume of any given surgical procedure to be safe and high-quality…and which do not and pose a danger to patients needing that procedure. Due to their network contracts, however, the BUCAHs refuse to inform and guide their members to the safe, high-volume hospitals.

---

6   Steve Sternberg and Geoff Dougherty, "Risks Are High at Low-Volume Hospitals," *U.S. News & World Report*, May 18, 2015, https://www.usnews.com/news/articles/2015/05/18/risks-are-high-at-low-volume-hospitals.

7   The Leapfrog Group, "Safety in Numbers: Hospital Performance on Leapfrog's Surgical Volume Standard," leapfroggroup.com, accessed November 11, 2021, https://www.leapfroggroup.org/sites/default/files/Files/Leapfrog%20Report%20on%20Safe%20Surgical%20Volumes%202020.pdf

Health-care Russian Roulette

Bottom line, the BUCAH insurance companies will not and cannot keep you safe from bad and even dangerous providers. By denying you provider quality scores, the BUCAHs force you to play Russian Roulette with your health and your life when choosing a doctor or hospital from their networks. You might get a world-class doctor — CLICK; you might get another Ramon Vazquez — BANG.

What are your odds of getting a bad, potentially dangerous physician or hospital? That's impossible to say, of course. But in Russian Roulette, the revolver usually has six chambers, one of which contains a live cartridge… so a 1 in 6 chance of the gun firing when you spin the cylinder and pull the trigger. Pretty lousy odds.

According to the *New England Journal of Medicine*, just *two percent* of physicians are responsible for 39% of medical malpractice claims paid in the U.S.[8] Let's assume — wrongly — for our purposes here that only two percent of doctors are dangerous. Two percent seems like a small risk, doesn't it? But if offered a jar of 100 aspirin tablets for your bad headache, would you take a couple of tablets if you knew that two — just two — of the 100 were *cyanide* tablets?

Life and death decisions in the C-Suite

Business owners and company executives, of course, would find absurd the idea of providing even a single employee an aspirin jar with 98 aspirin tablets and two cyanide tablets. That miniscule risk is totally unacceptable.

Yet every year, owners and executives in America's C-Suites make the decision to put their employees in BUCAH-managed health plans that intentionally conceal provider outcomes data from their plan members.

---

8   David M. Studdert et al, "Changes in Practice among Physicians with Malpractice Claims," *New England Journal of Medicine*. March 2019.

Most employer-sponsored healthcare plans are BUCAH fully insured health plans or self-insured plans managed by a BUCAH carrier under an "administrative services only" (ASO) agreement where the employer funds the health plan. Since both BUCAH fully insured plans and BUCAH ASO arrangements require use of the carrier's provider network, all BUCAH-managed health plans hide provider quality scores from the plan members.

That means that any plan run by a BUCAH carrier will force the members to choose their doctors and hospitals without the benefit of provider outcomes quality scores.

So, at every annual plan renewal, the C-Suite makes a decision regarding the company's healthcare plan that can have life and death implications for their employees. When owners and executives decide to put or keep employees in a BUCAH-managed plan, they unwittingly are putting the health and lives of their employees at risk.

In other words, every year when choosing their employees' healthcare plan, *employers are making life and death decisions in the C-Suite.*

When you see someone being forced to play Russian Roulette, don't you take away the gun? Once you realize that your current BUCAH health plan forces you and your employees to play healthcare Russian Roulette, unnecessarily putting you and your employees at risk, don't you want to remove the BUCAH plan and look for an alternative?

Plans that eliminate healthcare Russian Roulette

Is there an option for employers who want to stop putting their employees at risk from bad doctors and unsafe hospitals in BUCAH health plans?

Fortunately, employers have available a proven alternative model for employer-sponsored health plans known as NextGen Benefits, that is replacing health plans managed by the insurance companies.

The first step for the plan sponsor is to disintermediate the BUCAH insurance company. By eliminating this healthcare middleman, the owner or executive is now able to take control of the company's healthcare spend and, working with a NextGen Benefits adviser, put in place a new health plan that provides employees with objective quality data and expert guidance to select high-quality doctors and hospitals.

With their focus on quality medical outcomes, NextGen health plans help owners and executives eliminate the risky health-care Russian Roulette of the BUCAH plans.

Of course, replacing a BUCAH health plan with a NextGen plan to get different results means doing your employer-sponsored health plan differently. Replacing a fully insured BUCAH plan requires moving your health plan to a self-funded financing arrangement.

Self-funding your health plan

Business owners and executives do not need to be experts on healthcare plans and funding arrangements; that's why they have advisers and consultants on healthcare benefits. But too many business leaders consciously avoid self-funding because of myths and misunderstanding around self-funding.

First, properly done, self-funding your employee's healthcare plan involves absolutely no more financial risk than your fully insurance BUCAH carrier plan. You have zero financial risk from your self-funded plan beyond your maximum liability, which should be roughly what you pay in annual premium on your fully insured plan. This is because few businesses that self-fund are truly "self" funding;

most self-funded plans are what are known as "partially self-funded," due to the use of stop-loss insurance, which limits your maximum liability to a fixed dollar amount.

As a simplified example, let's say a company last year paid $1 million in premiums for a fully insured BUCAH health plan. That $1 million was the company's maximum liability; any healthcare claims above $1 million would be covered by the insurance company. Moving to a self-funded plan, the company again would have a maximum liability of $1 million, with a stop-loss insurance policy covering all medical and pharmacy claims above the $1 million. Any so-called catastrophic claim on the self-funded plan would be paid by the stop-loss carrier.

So self-funding done correctly is in no way the risky, unlimited financial exposure many believe it to be.

Perhaps more important for the company considering self-funding is that, in the fully-insured plan, $1 million was the company's both best and worst case scenario. $1 million was the company's maximum exposure, regardless of the actual cost of claims. But if the full $1 million wasn't spent on employee medical and pharmacy claims, all of the premium was non-refundable, that is, the insurance company keeps any surplus.

For example, in any health plan — fully or self-funded — there are two buckets of money. A fixed-cost *Administrative Expenses Bucket* of about 20 percent of the total plan funds and a variable-cost *Claims Bucket* with the remaining 80 percent to pay the employees' medical and pharmacy expenses. With $1 million in premiums, the claims bucket would contain about $800,000. If employees only spent $600,000 on healthcare that year, the plan would have a $200,000 surplus, which in a fully insured plan the insurance company would keep as profit. But in a self-funded plan, those funds are retained by the company.

For a company that already is self-funded but managed with a BUCAH ASO arrangement, a NextGen health plan only needs a change in plan management.

Independent third-party administrator

Instead of the BUCAH ASO, NextGen plans employ an independent third-party administrator (TPA) to manage the financial aspects of the plan, freeing the employer from any administrative responsibilities for the plan.

The TPA handles the claims processing and payment, enrollment, and other membership functions. Ensuring the quality and controlling the cost of healthcare falls to a standard business practice that NextGen plans apply to healthcare.

Healthcare supply chain management

NextGen plans ensure high quality healthcare for employees with a business practice that employers use in every other business unit in their company except healthcare: supply chain management.

Management of the healthcare supply chain is possible, however, only with disintermediation of the BUCAH carrier, which denies the employer — the payer! — the opportunity to apply any supply chain methodologies to the healthcare that employees purchase.

With that control, NextGen health plans manage the healthcare supply chain — first for quality, only then for cost — to deliver high-quality care at lower costs.

There are a number of strategies and tools that NextGen Benefits advisers use to manage the supply chain of healthcare, including:

- **medical utilization management**, which is central to informing and guiding of employees to high-quality providers;

- **patient advocacy**, which provides the patient with the right level of care;

- **medical claims repricing**, which addresses hospital overcharges;

- **pharmacy management**, which tackles the low-hanging fruit of high drug costs;

- **direct contracts** with providers, including surgeons and hospitals;

- **medical second opinions**, which prevent incorrect and unnecessary treatments and procedures; and

- **predictive data analytics**, which provides insights into future healthcare risks, allowing for preemptive action to eliminate or mitigate the risk.

For many NextGen plans, medical utilization management is the central nervous system of the plan, providing the provider quality data and guiding members to the high-quality providers.

The surgeon on call

Here's another true story that illustrates exactly how a NextGen health plan protects members from poor quality providers. In a bad fall at home, "Joan" suffered a traumatic spine fracture. Rushed by ambulance to the hospital, her injuries required emergency surgery, which would be performed by the on-call spine surgeon. After getting the name of the surgeon on call, Joan's daughter immediately submitted the surgeon's name to the concierge at the plan's medical utilization management firm for his quality data.

The surgeon on call had an outcomes score for spinal surgery of just **9.4**, **Very Poor**. The nurse concierge identified another surgeon with a **97.9**, **Excellent** quality score who had privileges at the hospital and was available for the surgery. This high-quality physician successfully performed the emergency surgery with no problems or complications.

When the daughter refused to allow the on-call surgeon to operate on her mother because of the poor quality score, no one at the hospital resisted the decision or seemed surprised at his low score. While they didn't know the actual score, the hospital staff knew the surgeon on call was not a good doctor.

It's tragic that the BUCAH plans also know the bad doctors but keep the information secret from their members, consigning their members to the "on call" doctor in a hospital emergency, regardless of the quality of care that will be delivered.

Unlike the BUCAH plans, NextGen health plans start with quality of care as the primary consideration, both when guiding members to healthcare providers and when managing the cost of care.

Quality first

Healthcare premiums have more than tripled in the past 20 years,[9] driven ever higher by healthcare costs that have increased every year since 1960.[10] During the past decade alone, employees' health plan deductibles have risen four times faster than wage increases.[11] Fully half of Americans with employer-sponsored insurance report putting off healthcare because of the out-of-pocket costs.[12]

---

9   Kaiser Family Foundation, "2020 Employer Health Benefits Survey," kff.org, October 8, 2020, https://www.kff.org/report-section/ehbs-2020-section-1-cost-of-health-insurance.
10   Centers for Medicare and Medicaid Services, "NHE Summary, including share of GDP, CY 1960-2019 (ZIP)," cms.gov, accessed November 17, 2021, https://www.cms.gov/Research-Statistics-Data-and-Systems/Statistics-Trends-and-Reports/NationalHealthExpendData/NationalHealthAccountsHistorical.
11   Kaiser Family Foundation, "Average Family Premiums Rose 4% to $21,342 in 2020, Benchmark KFF Employer Health Benefit Survey Finds," kff.org, October 8, 2020, https://www.kff.org/health-costs/press-release/average-family-premiums-rose-4-to-21342-in-2020-benchmark-kff-employer-health-benefit-survey-finds.
12   Kaiser Family Foundation, "Data Note: Americans' Challenges with Healthcare Costs," kff.org, https://www.kff.org/health-costs/issue-brief/data-note-americans-challenges-health-care-costs.

So, it's no surprise that the cost of healthcare dominates discussions at the dinner table and the conference table, not to mention in the halls of Congress. And certainly, the cost of healthcare has become a problem and a deterrent to Americans, even those with health insurance,

However, when it comes to healthcare, cost is important only when the quality of care is high. As Leah Binder, healthcare quality advocate and CEO of The Leapfrog Group, has observed, "There is no good price for bad healthcare." Indeed, what every patient really wants is affordable, *quality* healthcare.

Thus, the price of healthcare always is — and should be — a secondary consideration to quality. Except that, in our current system, the BUCAH insurance companies refuse to inform the patient which healthcare providers produce high-quality outcomes, and which are dangerous to the health and well-being of their patients.

NextGen plans, by starting with the quality of provider outcomes and guiding employees to the high-quality providers, put the emphasis where it should be: on the quality of care. This focus on quality has an unexpected effect on the cost of healthcare.

High-quality care, lower cost

When employees follow a NextGen health plan's guidance to high-quality doctors and facilities, the plan achieves remarkable savings. This is due to another healthcare secret: *The inverse relationship between quality and cost.* Although it's counterintuitive, the path to lower-cost healthcare is high-quality healthcare providers.

Put another way, you pay less for the highest quality providers that deliver better outcomes. For many reasons, the doctors, hospitals, and surgery centers that produce the best medical outcomes usually charge much less than their lower-quality competitors.

Savings to the company in a NextGen health plan are in the range of $2,000 per employee per year, sometimes more. These savings are due to a reduction in the company's overspend on healthcare, putting misallocated capital back on the company's balance sheet.

But the company is not the only financial beneficiary of a NextGen health plan.

Zero out-of-pocket costs

To encourage employees to follow the plan's guidance to high-quality providers, NextGen Benefits plan designs also greatly reduce or, in most cases, totally eliminate employee out-of-pocket costs.

When employees follow a NextGen health plan's guidance, the plan usually eliminates their out-of-pocket costs. This changes employee behavior around healthcare. When they have to pay thousands of dollars out of their own pocket for their healthcare, 50 percent of employees delay seeking medical care.[12] These delays often result in much more costly episodes of care, as their conditions worsen over time until they can no longer avoid care. This deferred care not only increases the cost to the employer, but unnecessarily risks the health of employees.

NextGen health plans allow employees to access care when first needed, at no out-of-pocket cost as long as they follow the guidance of the plan's medical utilization management team that screens for high-quality providers.

Since every patient wants high-quality, affordable healthcare and every employer wants an affordable and sustainable healthcare plan, this is a phenomenal win-win scenario.

Making the right life and death decision

No business owner or executive would consciously put the life and health of their employees at risk from a dangerous doctor or unsafe hospital. Providing employees with a BUCAH-managed healthcare plan that knowingly puts its members at risk is a life and death decision that no longer should be an acceptable business decision.

By replacing the BUCAH plan with a NextGen health plan, owners and executives are making the right life and death decision, *in favor of* the health and safety of their employees.

The choice of healthcare plan is a life and death decision in the C-Suite. The NextGen Benefits model lets the C-Suite make the right decision about healthcare, to provide employees with a quality-first healthcare plan that ensures high-quality providers with higher quality outcomes, at an affordable cost for the company, and with zero out-of-pocket costs for the employees.

That's an executive decision that everyone can live with.

Nelson Griswold

Founder & Chairman
NextGen Benefits Network

A controversial industry disrupter, bestselling author, and in-demand keynote speaker, Nelson Griswold is Founder and Chairman of the NextGen Benefits Network, a national alliance of independent healthcare advisory & consulting firms.

NextGen Benefits Network members are revolutionizing employee benefits and healthcare delivery by helping executives improve the quality of care and make healthcare a controllable cost by managing their company's healthcare supply chain. Their success and strategies have been featured in prominent business publications including *Chief Executive* and *CFO* magazines.

The author of *DO OR DIE*, a trade best-seller for leaders of employee benefits firms, he is lead author of two #1 bestsellers on healthcare reform, *BREAKING THROUGH THE STATUS QUO – How Innovative Companies Are Changing the Benefits Game to Help Their Employees and Boost Their Bottom Line* and *NEXTGENERATION HEALTHCARE – Proven Secrets of Managing the Healthcare Value Chain to Improve Outcomes and Reduce Costs.*

An authority and popular speaker on healthcare reform, Nelson has spoken in 46 states and the District of Columbia and has keynoted numerous conferences.

Nelson has been honored as a *Health Value Awards* Finalist at the World Health Care Congress and was presented the prestigious *Industry Leadership Award* by the Voluntary Benefits Association. He is a featured columnist for *Employee Benefit News* magazine and writes for other publications including *BenefitsPRO* and *Entrepreneur.*

CONTACT INFO ────────────────────────────

NextGen Benefits Network
(615)-369-0618
www.NextGenBenefits.Network

2

Debunking the Myths of Healthcare Quality

by Aaron Ault

MAGINE THAT YOU, FOR WHATEVER REASON, suddenly need to find a doctor. How do you do it? Many of us have experienced this exact situation. Thankfully, there are no end of resources available to help someone find a physician. An internet search for doctors in a specific area will likely return thousands of results, many of which have four and five star reviews. A social media post asking for recommendations will garner plentiful responses, with most of them claiming their doc is "the best." An insurance carrier website has countless recommendations available, along with assurances that the doctors they point to are "in network" for their subscribers. In fact, a relaxing evening of television will likely feature countless commercials for local doctors, all claiming to be the expert. Finding a doctor is not a difficult proposition.

It's making sure you find a good doctor.

That's because, in some ways, doctors are a lot like mechanics. They have very specialized knowledge, there are a lot of them, and there are both good ones and bad ones. Just as a person would likely want to make sure a specific mechanic is "up to snuff" before letting him or her work on their car, the same is certainly true for a doctor who will be working on their body. But how? There are remarkably few resources available to the public for evaluating doctors, which leaves most people relying on one of the avenues above, basing a potentially life-saving (or ending) decision on the shaky foundations of a friend's recommendation or a flashy television ad.

That's really bad news. Because these are not reliable sources for determining how good a doctor is, or evaluating the quality of the care they provide.

I've spent almost two decades working with an organization that specializes in connecting people with the highest quality healthcare available to them. Oftentimes, that involves steering people away from doctors they wanted to go to or were already working with, because those physicians were lacking in quality, and sending them to docs that weren't on their radar. Over the years, we've heard many explanations for why patients wanted to go to, did not want to go to, and would not switch from a specific doctor, but generally these reasons boil down to four principles. We call these the "Myths of Healthcare Quality."

Myth #1: Doctor Recommendations Are Always Right.

This particular line of reasoning is extremely common. Oftentimes, when someone finds out they need a new doctor it's because the physician they are currently receiving treatment from decides that whatever is going on is outside their expertise. So, the individual asks their current doctor who they should go to. It's a reasonable tactic, and one we see often.

This is what one of our patients did when she wanted to address a problem she was having. Gwen was peeing when she sneezed, a common problem for women as they age. Gwen asked her gynecologist about this issue and was told she would have to see a urologist if she wanted it fixed since it was a urological problem. Of course, since Gwen trusted her gynecologist, she asked her to recommend a urologist. Her gynecologist recommended Dr. Samuels. Gwen then phoned our call center and asked for help finding a good urologist, and specifically asked if we would recommend Dr. Samuels. Our nurse looked up urologists in Gwen's area and found several high quality physicians, all with objective quality ratings in what we consider the "A" range. Unfortunately, Dr. Samuels wasn't one of them. Dr. Samuels had an objective quality score of an "F," a score so low that we would never recommend a patient see that doctor. When we told Gwen the results, she was shocked . . . because Dr. Samuels was her gynecologist's husband.

There are plenty of reasons why a doctor would recommend another physician. Perhaps their practice is owned by a local health system that requires them to send a certain number of referrals to other doctors within the system.[1] Maybe the other doctor is a close friend, a golf buddy, or a family member.[2] Sometimes doctors only refer to those they genuinely think are the best fit, those they respect and admire. Unfortunately, however, the average doctor is not equipped to evaluate the objective quality of other doctors. And they shouldn't be expected to. Doctors are paid to be excellent physicians, not expert referral agents, so they are usually not a useful resource when you need a referral for a good physician.

Myth #2: Nurses Always Know the Good Doctors from the Bad Ones.

So, if a doctor isn't a good referral source for another physician, surely someone else must be. It would be reasonable to assume that a friend who works as a nurse might be a good source. After all, this person is in the medical field, likely works with numerous doctors on a day-to-day basis, and gets to see behind the curtain and into the backrooms of medicine. Even more than that, they're trustworthy — nurses have been voted the most trusted occupation every year for almost two decades.[3] For these reasons, nurses are often a go-to for doctor recommendations.

Oftentimes, however, nurses are not equipped to make objective judgments on a physician's quality. This is primarily due to two factors. First, depending on the setting, a nurse's exposure to a specific doctor may be extremely limited. A nurse working on a floor dedicated to patients recovering from back surgery would have very little regular interaction with a cardiologist, despite the fact that they work at the same hospital. An ER nurse may have worked with a neurosurgeon on a few isolated cases, but it would be a stretch to call them "familiar" with each other. Second, a nurse's perspective of a doctor is based on a different set of criteria than a patient's would be; the doctor is being evaluated as their coworker, not as their physician, because that is the context in which their interactions take place. Typically, nurses can speak to the workplace behavior and perhaps bedside manner of doctors they work with, but not to their quality.

My mother is a registered nurse and worked as a cardiac ICU nurse at a well-regarded local hospital for many years. She told me a story recently about a doctor she knew during her time there who we will call Dr. Roberts. Dr. Roberts treated the cardiac ICU nurses very well. He often left donuts and coffee in the nurse break room, a much appreciated boon for the third shift staff, and would send flowers to the nurse's station whenever a long-term patient passed away. Understandably, Dr. Roberts was very well regarded by the nursing staff at that hospital. My mother said that, at the time, if someone had asked her what she thought of Dr. Roberts, she would have said he was "an awesome guy," and if someone asked for her recommendation for a cardiologist, Dr. Roberts would have come to mind. Recently, she looked up Dr. Roberts' quality score. It was low enough that we would never recommend him to our patients. He was a very good coworker, but that did not make him a good physician.

Nurses have a limited amount of data. Much of what they know about the doctors they work with is based on interactions at the patient bedside or in the break room. They don't intentionally give out bad recommendations; they just don't have access to the data that matters, information like readmission, complications, or mortality, the sort of information that determines a physician's objective quality.

Myth #3: The Head of the Department is the Best Doctor.

So, if neither doctors nor nurses can point to good doctors with any sort of accuracy, where should people turn? Some people put their trust in the administration of the hospital they will be using. For example, when looking for an oncologist, they choose the head of the oncology department at their local hospital. It happens all the time — in cases where we have to steer patients away from the doctor they chose, an all-too-common response is, "But he's the head of the department! How could he be a low quality doctor?" This is born out of an understandable assumption: that the person in charge of something must be the best at that thing, otherwise they would not be in charge. By this logic, for example, the person in charge of the cardiology department at the local hospital must be the best cardiologist. While this is occasionally correct, and is certainly correct in other fields, oftentimes in medicine there is little correlation between a physician's status as a department head and their objective quality.

We recently worked with a patient, let's call her Jessica, who was diagnosed with a recurrence of gastric cancer — a cancer of the stomach that was treated previously but had returned. She wanted to be treated at a well known and well regarded facility by Dr. Baker. Our nurses researched the facility and found that it had a poor quality score — in "review" terms, it would have received one out of five stars. Even worse, Dr. Baker's quality score for the type of treatment this patient needed was abysmal. We presented this information to Jessica and recommended she seek care elsewhere, and provided other recommendations for high quality options. She refused, saying, "He's the head of the department, your data must just be wrong." Jessica was right — Dr. Baker headed the appropriate department at that hospital. In fact, he held several such positions at that hospital with titles like "Director" and "Chairman". He did Jessica's surgery. Afterward, she was hospitalized more than twice as long as she should have been for that procedure. A few weeks after she was discharged, she was readmitted for complications associated with the procedure.

Department Heads are not necessarily the best doctors in their department. It seems counterintuitive, but it's often true. This is because being a great department head requires different skills than being a great doctor. In modern medicine, many of the responsibilities of the head of a department are administrative rather than clinical. Job recruiting site Ziprecruiter advises that the responsibilities of a department head like a chief of surgery include "being part of hospital research efforts, evaluating surgical personnel, participating in medical education programs, and looking for quality improvement opportunities for the hospital surgical staff."[4] It then stands to reason that a key qualification for those promoted to the department head position would be a proficiency for these sorts of tasks, rather than necessarily being the best doctor.

Myth #4: My Doctor Always Knows the Best Treatment for My Condition.

The job of ensuring healthcare quality does not stop when the doctor search does. As challenging as it is to steer someone away from a poor quality doctor before they have their first appointment, the task becomes exponentially more difficult when there is a pre-existing relationship. This is because people have an implicit trust in their doctor, even more than in their lawyer or priest.[5] We hear this from patients all the time: "I'm sure my doctor knows what's best", or "My doctor knows my case". What they are really saying is, "The treatment my doctor recommends must be the right one". Unfortunately, however, a pre-existing and positive doctor-patient relationship does not ensure objective quality, nor does it necessarily mean a doctor's recommendations will be correct. Doctor's aren't infallible.

In 2018 we handled a case involving a patient diagnosed with cancer. We'll call him Charles. The physician handling Charles' treatment requested authorization for him to undergo a specific type of chemotherapy. We gathered all the relevant information, including medical studies, Charles' records, and his insurance plan design. Then we brought in our team of physicians to review the case. Based on the evidence, as well as a "peer-to-peer" discussion between our physicians and Charles' doctor, the treatment was ruled "experimental/investigational", or not an approved treatment for Charles' condition. As such, we determined that the proposed chemotherapy was not appropriate for Charles and would not be approved. He was advised to pursue a different course of treatment with a different physician.

In that discussion, it was uncovered that Charles' doctor did not evaluate his liver function, and our physicians were concerned that Charles' liver would not be able to process the treatment (poor liver function would be considered a red flag or "contraindication" for the proposed treatment). Charles' employer, however, elected to have another organization evaluate his case. That organization advised that they would have approved this treatment in this situation. Based on that recommendation, his employer overrode our decision and approved the treatment. Once Charles' doctor found out the treatment was approved, he administered the chemotherapy we denied. Twelve days later Charles was dead. The experimental/investigational chemotherapy caused his liver to fail.

No doctor, not even the very best, is infallible. No one doctor can know every piece of essential information for every possible condition they could encounter. That's because today the total amount of medical knowledge doubles every seventy-three days.[6] Even assuming that a new doctor has a firm grip on every single piece of medical knowledge available on graduation day (at best an impractical assumption), this means that without constant study, on top of seeing patients, managing their practice, and maintaining their personal lives, doctors fall farther and farther behind. Because of this, your doctor might not know the best treatment for your condition. A good doctor, one with a high objective quality score, combats this by making treatment decisions based on all available medical evidence, not just what they are familiar with, and they accept the counsel of qualified experts.

So What Can Be Done?

The truth behind these common myths paints a grim picture — that of a world where every doctor's visit is a roll of the dice, and a gamble on that physician's quality with the highest of stakes. It's a challenging dilemma — patients need to make educated decisions on where they receive their healthcare, but they lack any way to reliably access the objective information they need to make those decisions.

Thankfully, there is a solution. An experienced, effective medical management organization will not only have access to that information, but also the expertise to guide patients to quality providers and evaluate the treatment recommendations of those providers to ensure patients receive the best quality care they can.

Endnotes

1 Mathews, A. W., & Evans, M. (2018, December 27). *The hidden system that explains how your doctor makes referrals.* The Wall Street Journal. Retrieved from https://www.wsj.com/articles/the-hidden-system-that-explains-how-your-doctor-makes-referrals-11545926166.

2 *What's behind that medical referral?* US News. (n.d.). Retrieved from https://health.usnews.com/health-news/patient-advice/articles/2016-04-07/whats-behind-that-medical-referral.

3 Saad, L. (2021, August 13). *U.S. ethics ratings rise for medical workers and teachers.* Gallup.com. Retrieved from https://news.gallup.com/poll/328136/ethics-ratings-rise-medical-workers-teachers.aspx.

4 *What is a chief of surgery.* ZipRecruiter. (n.d.). Retrieved from https://www.ziprecruiter.com/e/What-Is-a-Chief-of-Surgery.

5 McCarthy, N. (2021, June 29). *America's most & least trusted professions [infographic].* Forbes. Retrieved from https://www.forbes.com/sites/niallmccarthy/2019/01/11/americas-most-least-trusted-professions-infographic/?sh=65fe250e7e94.

6 Densen, P. (2011). *Challenges and opportunities facing medical education.* Transactions of the American Clinical and Climatological Association. Retrieved from https://www.ncbi.nlm.nih.gov/pmc/articles/PMC3116346.

Aaron Ault

CFO
Ault International Medical
Management

AARON AULT serves as the Managing Partner of Osprey Benefit Advisors and the CFO of AIMM. He has been involved with AIMM since its founding and assisted in the development of both the P3CM process and the Bridge Program. In 2021, he founded Osprey Benefit Advisors in order to take the innovative strategies making healthcare affordable directly to employers and their employees. Previously, he worked with several non-profit organizations including the Nazarene Foundation and the Arkansas Dream Center. He graduated from Mount Vernon Nazarene University in 2017 and is currently pursuing a master's degree.

CONTACT INFO

To learn how to build quality resources into your plan, go to:
www.ospreybenefits.com/contactus
Or download our primer at: https://bit.ly/2SUnTi9
(614)-905-1770
aaron@ospreybenefits.com
www.ospreybenefits.com

3

The Truth About "Quality" Healthcare — Hard Lessons Learned from Personal Experience

by Randy Hansen & Nick Hansen

HERE'S A TRUE STORY ABOUT how Americans blindly trust that their doctor will provide quality healthcare.

Nana, our mom/grandmother was a healthy, tough eighty-two-year-old Norwegian who lived alone, cared for her home, her yard, her family and herself. Based on all signs, she seemed like the perfect candidate to become a centenarian. One hundred years wouldn't even be a challenge for her! Then one day as Nana was walking the recycling bin to the end of her driveway, she tripped and fell (Side note: It's 28 degrees and clear outside). She does not call 9-1-1. Rather, she phones her grandson Nick to tell him she won't be able to have him over for dinner that evening because she fell. We told you she was tough!

Fortunately for Nana, a kind neighbor happened to be walking by and noticed her on the driveway. After assessing the situation, they immediately called 9-1-1. Paramedics arrive, diagnose a broken right leg, and proceed to take her to our trusted local hospital. Upon getting the news, we meet her in the ER. After numerous x-rays, it was determined that she had a clean break to her femur bone just above her artificial knee. She broke it good! The staff at the hospital, following a tradition of great care in our community, suggested that they operate on Nana the next day with, who they referred to as, a "high quality" orthopedic surgeon who was available to do the surgery.

Being a caring family, we wanted to meet the doctor first, so we 'interviewed' him! Sure enough, he went to a prestigious medical school, had years of experience, and a great bedside manner. We loved the guy, but more importantly, so did Nana. With all the confidence in the world, we anxiously awaited her surgery so she could get back to life as normal.

In the morning we all see Nana off to her surgery. Time passes slowly. Finally, after nearly five hours, the doctor comes in and shares that she did great! He said she had lost a lot of blood, which they replaced, and that she should be ready to be transferred to a rehab facility in a day or two. Fast forward a few weeks. Nana's physical health was good, but her right foot would not cooperate with the rest of her leg. Seems she just can't control it, so off we go to meet with a specialist. This is important! We have a young eighty-two-year-old, who isn't challenged by getting to 100, that has lost the use of her right foot. Walking, driving a car, climbing in and out of a shower… all things that need an active right foot are lost.

After numerous visits with multiple physicians, it is determined that the surgeon damaged a nerve during her surgery. Irreversible! Not coming back! It was like Mike Tyson just knocked her to the canvas and she was not getting back up. In fairness to the doctor, we all signed a waiver prior to surgery that releases him from any risks and complications resulting from the surgery. We knew going in there was a chance of a less than desirable outcome. But here we are today, five years later and Nana can't drive, has to walk with a walker, and has moved into an assisted living facility. We still believe that 100 years old is well within her capability, but the quality of those years took a severe blow!

Here is where things get interesting. While looking for more ways to improve the quality of care for our healthcare consulting clients, we found a vendor who offers unbiased, factual ratings on physicians. These are not Yelp or other subjective opinion reviews, but objective data on things like readmission rates, infection rates, complication rates, morbidity, mortality, surgeon board certification, and whether there are sanctions against their license, etc. Essentially, the things that do/should matter when choosing a doctor or surgeon to take care of you. This has proven to be a great tool in helping the employees of our clients find the highest rated provider possible — without having to rely on a brief interview to check out the doctor's 'bedside manner'. This is a game changer for finding the best and most qualified person for any and all care an employee or their family might need. This tool would likely have changed the outcome for Nana and her future.

Two years ago we finally had the courage to look up the ratings for Dr. Surgeon, the person who did Nana's surgery. Dr. Surgeon had a 12.5 rating (1-100 rating system, with 100 being the best). Our hearts ached. I (Randy) recently had minor knee surgery and looked at local surgeon ratings beforehand. I chose a doctor that rated 98 over the ones coming in at 31 and 40. Here we are, doing due diligence on Randy's minor knee surgery. There's no way we are allowing a doctor rated 40 to do surgery when there is a 98 available! Yet, Nana's three sons interviewed Dr. Surgeon and agreed on him because he had a good degree, years of experience, and was nice. We didn't know about his 12.5 rating, but we will take that huge mistake to our graves. This was one of those moments in life where you just wish you could have a do-over.

The hard truth about a situation like Nana's is that in most cases, there are no do-overs. No taking the car back to the shop to have the faulty brakes replaced at no additional cost. You have one shot at getting it right. We're obviously very lucky that her poor outcome only led to the limited use of one of her feet (we use "only" very loosely as she'd obviously love to have that mobility back). With a quality score as low as her surgeon's, it could have been much worse.

As a C-Level employee at your company, you not only have an obligation to protect the balance sheet, but you likely feel an obligation to take care of your employees as an extension of your own family. This is where desired outcomes can begin to seem complicated. Most people are preconditioned to think that in order to achieve the highest level of care, you must go to the biggest, most well-known facilities around — large, local, not-for-profit hospitals! While you can find very highly rated surgeons at these types of facilities, the truth is, they aren't the only game in town.

Another question you should be asking yourself is why you haven't had access to this type of data in the past. Surely if Nick and Randy at PSG Washington from Everett, WA have access to this data, a multi-billion-dollar insurance company would too. Well, they do have access to this data, but steering your employees to high quality care isn't their top priority. In reality, spreading opportunities to members of their network is more important. Don't believe us? Head over to the website of one of the country's largest health insurance carriers and run a generic provider search in any particular specialty (make sure they aren't being sorted by name, location, etc.). Now run the exact same search three or four days later. Did the same doctors show up on both searches? Likely not, as the search engine is on a rotation aiming to give doctors an equal opportunity at access to patients. Call me crazy, but picking a doctor based on their availability when you need surgery or because it was their turn to show up in the search results doesn't sound like the best way to make decisions as important as this.

We've spent a lot of time talking about quality of care, but that doesn't mean we've forgotten about what likely led to you opening this book in the first place: your bottom line. In fact, when you start to pay more attention to quality of care, you'll start to see your cost of claims actually decrease. In healthcare, high cost definitely does not equal high quality.

In the Seattle market, where we live, you can go to a local hospital that will remain nameless and have a knee replacement surgery that will cost your plan about $27,000. Luckily for you, that hospital is considered in-network for the insurance plan you have, so the price you paid was generously discounted off the chargemaster rate. A win for you, right? Not so much. You could also have gone to a local ambulatory surgery center, had the exact same surgeon perform the surgery, and the plan would have only been charged $9,000. Same surgery. Same surgeon. Same outcome. But $18,000 in savings.

Most importantly, take this away from our comments:

You can have access to the highest quality provider in the specialty you need. No more blind guessing or subjective referral/provider lists. All while lowering your overall costs. Contrary to popular belief in the C-Suite, healthcare is a controllable cost.

Randy Hansen & Nick Hansen

PSG Washington

RANDY HANSEN and **NICK HANSEN** are a father and son team and employee benefits consultants at PSG Washington in Everett, WA. Randy is the co-author of the Amazon bestselling healthcare book, *Breaking Through the Status Quo*. Nick was named a Rising Star in Advising by Employee Benefit Advisor magazine in 2020. The two have partnered with c-suite executives across the country to help their organization manage a top three line item (healthcare) that often doesn't receive the attention it deserves. By putting the right pieces in place, their clients are lowering their healthcare spend by thousands of dollars per employee per year, offering plans that have $0 deductibles, $0 out of pocket maximums, and $0 copays for high priced specialty drugs, all while providing members with the highest level of care available.

CONTACT INFO

Randy Hansen
randy@psgwa.com
425-426-2096

Nick Hansen
nick@psgwa.com
425-426-2094

4

The Consequences
of Bad Healthcare

by Mark Grisanti

Starbucks spends more on healthcare for employees than coffee beans — Since 2008!

HOWARD SCHULTZ RETURNED AS THE CEO of Starbucks in January of 2008 when things were nearly at their worst. The company was opening seven new stores per day and their business model had spiraled out of control. At this time in the company's historic turnaround he was famously quoted as saying that the healthcare line item at Starbucks, which had tallied to well above $300 million annually, was more than what the company spent on coffee beans. This was an alarming statement to the average coffee consumer, who couldn't fathom what three hundred million dollars' worth of coffee beans might even look like sitting in a huge warehouse or packed into an assortment of trucks awaiting delivery. But for CEOs and CFOs, those ultimately responsible for providing employee benefits like medical insurance to their employees, it was a painful reminder of a problem that had existed for many years before — ever-increasing health insurance costs. For them, health insurance expenses consistently registered as their second largest line item after payroll well before Howard Schultz saved the day for Starbucks.

This is nothing new. It is no secret that C-Level executives are focused on the cost of healthcare and the impact this line item has to their bottom line. But knowing there is a problem and actually doing something to fix it are not always mutually exclusive when it comes to employer-sponsored health insurance programs. In fact, most executives manage every other major budget line item down to the dollar, but they will accept the status quo way of tackling their health insurance budget. Rather than see a healthcare plan for what it is — a supply chain that can be broken apart and effectively managed — they work with an insurance broker who plays the see-saw negotiation game every year with a handful of insurance carriers, and who has convinced them that a single digit increase to health insurance premiums is a win. Of course, not knowing any better, they take it and are even grateful it wasn't worse — already thinking about next year and hoping for the same result. The "expert" broker tends to also be an expert personal relationship manager who always pays for lunch, but who is incentivized and paid by the same insurance carriers passing along those double-digit premium increases year after year.

More premium and less benefit is always bad news for the employer, especially during open enrollment communications to staff, but it's good news for the lunch buyer. He has made a small fortune while working just a few weeks each year for his client and pocketing a percentage of the premiums paid on the first of every month since the beginning of the business relationship. The biggest benefit decisions at the company are often made by an HR staff overburdened with administrative tasks, who need to be up on the latest legislation, and who may not be privy to the company's financial risk tolerance or cash-flow standing—at least consistently or to the extent that it would be used strategically in those decisions. And that's not to say the HR staff isn't vital to the employee-benefits program or renewal process—they truly are. But while the HR team might be exceptional at what they do, they may not be in the best position to make financial decisions that involve risk-tolerance for the company on their own, without having the same insight into the intimate financials that the executive has.

As the CEO or CFO, running your business would be considerably easier if your health insurance costs could be controlled long-term. If you had a magic wand to waive once or twice over your next invoice, you would likely sign up right now if it meant just keeping premiums level for the next few years, never mind reducing them. The only problem (other than the fact that you don't have a magic wand, and if you did you would probably use it for something much cooler than this) is you have been told time and time again by many "experts" that controlling healthcare costs is simply not possible. No, you must accept that this line item is going to get more expensive each year regardless of what you do, and not only that, it is going to go up faster than any of your other line items—all because the healthcare industry says so! It might be funny if it wasn't also true. The truth is, the healthcare industry as a whole—everyone from your broker to the insurance carrier to the big hospital systems to the pharmacy where you pick up your prescriptions—has convinced you that these costs simply increase each year. So here's a question: Does anyone else see a problem with the fact that not one person in this supply chain of enormous profits and exploding stock prices—not one person who happens to be profiting more than the doctors providing the care who spent their entire twenties in medical school — is able to explain *exactly* why that is? Why do these costs go up and why can't they go down — ever?

A light at the end of the tunnel

The good news is there is a light at the end of this tunnel. It does exist. Fortunately, many CEOs and CFOs have, in fact, broken through the status quo situation referenced earlier. They have respectfully moved on from their personal relationship-focused benefits brokers and engaged healthcare advisers with the right experience and real solutions. These are consultants who have skin in the game and who will not only discuss ways to reduce healthcare spend, but also share how to actually "improve" the healthcare your employees are receiving. If your question is, "Can a benefits consultant actually help improve the healthcare our employees are receiving?" The answer is, well, why not? For the kind of money many of them make, is it not reasonable to expect them to do more than send a few emails to the carriers to shop your plan and conduct a few webinars at open enrollment? Good consultants use a variety of approaches and focus on proven solutions that make poor care more costly and difficult to utilize, while rewarding good care which increases good care outcomes. More on this in a moment.

Bad Healthcare vs Good Healthcare — Your Next Biggest Problem

What do you call the doctor who graduated at the bottom of his or her class in medical school? You call them doctor, as you should. But let's have that sink in for a minute. Yes, there is good healthcare and there is bad healthcare, just as there are good doctors and bad doctors. And with a good doctor practicing good healthcare you will more than likely achieve a good healthcare outcome — which is of course the ultimate goal any time you get sick or injured.

As a C-Level executive, while you work toward reducing what you pay annually for benefits each year, your healthcare adviser is responsible for making sure that for every dollar you spend, you get something positive back on your investment. Because what is the point of paying thousands, if not millions of dollars, for a healthcare program each year if it doesn't even provide your employees with good care? This is the role of an insurance adviser today, at least one that earns their money. If you're not working with someone who is having that discussion with you today, it's time to find yourself an adviser who can do both.

Howard Schultz was one of many chief executive officers to communicate how difficult and expensive it is to provide health insurance benefits to your employees. However, the next frontier in the ever-changing landscape of employer-sponsored health insurance will also be on the decision makers — the CEOs and CFOs who are charged with the responsibility of ensuring they get the **best results** for their investment in healthcare **benefits,** not just insurance. As the title of this book boldly states, C-Level executives are faced with "life-or-death decisions" every day — and now more than ever when it comes to the type of healthcare offered at your company. Therefore, the question remains; is your significant investment in this healthcare line item producing Good Healthcare, or Bad Healthcare for those premiums you're paying?

Good Healthcare — Medical Standard of Care

How do we define Good Healthcare? When we pick a doctor to treat us and the relationship has been established, we put our faith and confidence in them. If we get sick, we literally put our lives in their hands! Our doctors are responsible for providing care and treatments to the best of their abilities and our trust in choosing them is that their only goal will be to heal us, cure us, or to do their best to prevent our condition from deteriorating further. The diagnosis or treatments may differ from case to case, but our general expectation is that the doctor we select will deliver at what the legal dictionary defines as the "Medical Standard of Care".

The medical standard of care is the standard required of doctors and other medical personnel. In other words, the medical standard of care refers to the idea that a doctor possessing the same knowledge and skills as any other doctor owes his patients the best possible treatment and care they can provide. If there is a reasonable treatment option available and he or she does not pursue it, and the patient suffers as a result, then the doctor may be subject to a lawsuit for neglecting the patient under the medical standard of care.

Bad Healthcare — Medical Malpractice

What is Bad Healthcare? You would be hard-pressed to find someone interested in that. The relationship with our doctor is sacred, we trust them, we count on them to do the right thing — every time, with no exceptions. We need our doctors to heal us when we are sick or injured. Of course, there is the possibility that even if your doctor does everything "by the book", or in other words he or she follows the "medical standard or care", a bad outcome may still result. These are considered tragic cases, particularly when the doctor did everything right. But what if the doctor does not follow the medical standard of care or he/she makes an error? And what if as a result of that error someone does not get better, or worse, they perish?

Medical Malpractice is, in a nutshell, a form of negligence. Therefore, medical malpractice translates to mean that a doctor either did something wrong or did not exercise reasonable care when treating a patient. Medical malpractice exists if another reasonable doctor in that doctor's position would have treated the patient differently. Consider the following example which better illustrates the meaning of medical malpractice and the standard of care:

Allison, an expectant mother, believes she is in labor so she drives to the hospital. The attending doctor is in a rush so she looks Allison over quickly, tells her she is only having Braxton-Hicks contractions, and sends her home.

Allison leaves the hospital, but upon arriving home, she realizes she is about to give birth. Her husband calls 9-1-1 and tries to help her deliver the baby, but the umbilical cord wraps around the baby's neck. The baby has difficulty breathing, but when the EMTs arrive they are able to save the baby's life. The ambulance then takes Allison and her baby to a different hospital for aftercare.

In this case, Allison has the right to sue the doctor at the first hospital for medical malpractice. The doctor sent her home when she was clearly in labor, and her baby nearly died as a result. Another doctor in this situation would have examined Allison more thoroughly, realized she was in labor, and made the necessary preparations to help her bring her baby into the world safely.

Unfortunately, failure to meet medical standards of care are rather common today. And while some of the worst examples occur in the doctor's office, many can and do occur in the operating room as well. In some cases, if the doctor is negligent in prescribing the right medication or ordering the right surgery, the patient may suffer worse effects from the condition or even die. All of this means that the impetus to find the best care needs to fall on someone's shoulders. Is the employee responsible for making sure they receive good healthcare while submitting their claims through your plan? Surely employees make the best, most responsible managers of their own healthcare, don't they?

How Employees Select Doctors and Make Their Own Healthcare Decisions

Let's for a moment take an overly practical and simplified look at the way most working Americans access their own care today. The truth is, the large majority of working people throughout the country will literally put their LIVES into the hands of a doctor they know absolutely nothing about when they choose them. They know and, in most cases, have accepted that there is limited research the average person can do about a doctor's past, unless that doctor has experienced a lawsuit. Not to mention HIPAA privacy laws are confusing enough that most people don't want to go anywhere near discussing another person's healthcare experience with the doctor. So, what do most people do? They end up putting their faith, trust, and in many cases their lives in the hands of someone whom they have:

- Never met or perhaps met once in passing or heard about
- No research and no sense of prior healthcare outcomes for
- Limited understanding with how long they have been practicing medicine

Yes, although this may arguably be the most important decision a person will make during their lifetime, they will choose a doctor based on:

- Asking a neighbor or family member if they know a "good doctor"
- How close the doctor's office is to their home or work
- Whether or not the doctor's office is able to offer virtual healthcare appointments
- If they get a "good vibe" or they "trust their gut" after one meeting

- If the doctor participates as one of the tens of thousands of doctors in their insurance company's network (provided by their employer)
- They were recommended by another doctor (with whom the referring doctor is affiliated with — financially!)
- OR they were given a recommendation from HR, their employer's insurance broker, or a benefits administrator (*note: the insurance carrier is usually very careful not to "recommend" a provider to a benefit participant. They will share the contact information for a doctor in their provider network under a certain specialty, however they tend to be very careful about recommendations. As with most things done by the carriers, there is a reason for that*)

Just as C-Level executives will often pay more attention to less expensive line items than healthcare, employees will consistently place the importance of their own healthcare behind that of loved ones, friends, and even co-workers. Even when they do get sick and need to see a doctor, too often the amount of effort they will place into researching to find the right one is less than the effort they put into what they want to have for dinner. What are the consequences of all this?

Consequences of Bad Healthcare for the C-Suite

Imagine a nightmare scenario. An employee is sick and chooses to see a doctor who is accepted by your insurance carrier's network. An error is made by the doctor and a bad healthcare outcome for the employee is the result. Not only that, but the doctor who made the error did not follow the medical standard of care. When informed, the family of the employee proceeds with legal action, and it is noted by their attorney that the provider was participating in the health insurance plan that you as the CEO or CFO of the organization selected, sponsored, and paid for. The employee claims he was forced to make a change from his preferred doctor because the new insurance plan your broker provided, which you selected this year to save some money, did not include him in their provider network.

Can you as the CEO or CFO be held responsible for the consequences of this Bad Healthcare Outcome for one of your employees? Perhaps we can agree that the insurance carrier is not likely to jump at the opportunity to face the blame for contracting with a bad doctor. Even more likely, they might stress that they did not make a recommendation to use the provider, in this example. Yes, a nightmare.

For the average person with no affiliation to the healthcare industry outside of their own care and the care of their family, the thought of holding a CEO or CFO responsible for a bad healthcare outcome would never cross their mind. Even those actively working within the employer-sponsored health insurance industry may view the concept as a stretch because it has not happened, yet. However, there have been recent instances where this discussion is happening and where there's smoke, there's usually fire. The truth is, it isn't a matter of IF an employee will sue their employer for a bad healthcare outcome, it's a matter of when the first case will go to court. And the consequences of that case's result will have a lasting impact on how the average employer decides to protect themselves, forever.

Protect yourself, your company, and your employees—Offer Good Healthcare

What can you do today as a CEO or CFO of a great company responsible to (and in some cases required to) offer health insurance benefits to your employees? If your answer is to demand more from your BUCA carrier (Blue Cross, United Healthcare, Cigna, Aetna), good luck. These gargantuan companies are motivated by many things, but ensuring their members receive great care is low on the totem pole. The carriers are in the business of separating you from your money first, and helping you second. They have hundreds of programs to sell you which they say will improve care, but rarely do any of them do much more than upset the end user or end up costing you more money than they save. Counting on them would be accepting the status quo, which includes agreeing that your health insurance costs are "supposed to" go up by 8-12% every year. If the carriers were able to make sure that your healthcare plan was priced appropriately and that your employees were always receiving good care, wouldn't they be doing that already? Most of them have had decades to get it right. None of them have.

You can't possibly be an expert in all thing's healthcare. But what you can do is handle this line item with the appropriate level of awareness and attention that it deserves as your second or third largest. It all starts and ends with the people whom you trust to handle your program, your advisers. Most insurance brokers don't know how to, or really care to, do much more than email claims back and forth to the carrier when one of your employee's receives a denial, spreadsheet a handful of insurance carrier alternatives for you at your benefits renewal, and present to your employees during open enrollment. And don't forget, as premiums go up, so do their commissions and incentive bonuses.

Most brokers are content with the status quo. They want to string the current system out for as long as *you* can possibly afford to let them. They're on borrowed time. But they are great at buying lunch.

When you have had enough of the status quo and you're ready to break free, find a non-traditional benefits consultant who has years of experience in developing value-based plans from the ground up.

Someone who sees the healthcare program for what it is: a supply chain that can be broken up and managed effectively.

Your consultant needs to be many things, including all things healthcare, and needs to have a plan for your specific healthcare program that suits your needs, the needs of your company, and most importantly, the needs of your employees and their dependents. Your ideal consultant should have qualifications that include, at minimum:

- An ability to reduce the actual cost of care for all 4 of the major healthcare expense areas (Inpatient, Outpatient, Pharmacy, Provider Visits)
- An ability to positively impact the Quality of Healthcare, both in the short and long term, in a way that works well for your unique company and employees
- A unique capability to review data and access to Predictive Modeling Software
- ERISA Compliance expertise
- Efficient Employee Communication capabilities both during Open Enrollment and throughout the year
- Expansive Expertise in Self-funding and Alternative Funding plans
- An understanding and experience with Reference Based Pricing
- Empathy, Integrity, and Honesty

Comparing fees from one consultant to the next is not an efficient measure of their ability to support one of your largest and most important expenses. Their fees are a small piece of the overall healthcare pie. Instead, make sure you and your consultant have aligned incentives and that they are fully transparent with how they are compensated. A good consultant who is certain in their ability to perform all of the above will be open to placing a portion of their fees at risk, or will dedicate a portion of their compensation to a percentage of savings.

If these are conversations your current adviser has not had with you, maybe it's time to ask. When you do, ask them if they are consistently expanding their knowledge and experience each year, and how. One way to confirm if they are motivated to improve at their trade is to ask if they are NexGen Benefits certified — this is a qualified network of professionals who have attained all these traits and who meet regularly to share ideas. Much as your doctor refers to the work for their entire career as "practicing medicine", the role of the benefits consultant has changed drastically, and it has become critical in recent years to be able to count on them to do more. The good ones are regularly practicing healthcare program delivery and developing their knowledge to bring solutions to your problems, new and old. Demand more from your benefits consultant or find one you can trust. It's a life-or-death decision.

Mark Grisanti

Senior Vice President,
Employee Benefits Team Leader
Opus Advisory Group

Since the start of Mark's employee benefits career in 2002, his mission has been to utilize creative solutions to combat the ever-increasing cost of healthcare. Never one to accept the "status quo" in any situation, he was determined to understand the most intimate details of the healthcare industry. His desire to reevaluate and improve on the way that employers mitigated healthcare costs led him to Opus Advisory Group, where he has served as Lead Consultant and Employee Benefits Team Leader since 2006. Mark's practical understanding of client service needs and his ability to consistently reduce healthcare spending for any employer faced with this challenge have led to the expansive growth and trusted reputation Opus enjoys today

Mark is a published author who has appeared in Crain's New York, Newsday, LifeHealthPro, and in several industry trade journals. He has been bestowed one of the insurance industry's coveted Rising Star in Healthcare Consulting awards, and is nationally recognized as a Top Gun in Insurance

Mark holds a Bachelor's degree in Business Management from Pace University's Lubin School of Business.

CONTACT INFO ————————————————————————

Connect with Mark on LinkedIn at:
https://www.linkedin.com/in/markgrisanti
(914)-798-1057
Mark_Grisanti@opusadvisory.com
www.opusadvisory.com

5

The Ostrich Syndrome

by Tammera Hollerich

I MAGINE YOUR BUSINESS IS YOUR CHILD. We'll call her Cindy. Unfortunately, one day Cindy is in a horrible accident and ends up in the hospital. Critical medical decisions need to be made and they will affect Cindy for the rest of her life. Would you stick your metaphorical head in the sand and leave those decisions to some random patient down the hall? Of course you wouldn't. But when it comes to one of the biggest decisions affecting the financial life of your company, that's exactly what most CEOs do.

For more than 25 years I've been finding the right employee benefits packages for business owners. Almost invariably, when I go to present them to the CEO, I'm escorted down the hall to the HR department.

Most CEOs are under the impression employee benefits are an HR decision, but because benefits are typically the second largest line item on your profit and loss statement, the exact opposite should be happening. HR should be escorting me to the C-suite.

While your HR department might be excellent at relaying information to your employees, they generally have little to no knowledge about your company's finances. Putting decisions about your healthcare plan in the hands of HR is akin to asking the patient down the hall to make Cindy's medical decisions. You might as well be playing Russian roulette with the financial health of your company.

Every day, countless critical financial decisions that impact your bottom line are made by the C-suite. Your benefits package and the complexities inherent in it need to be included in those decisions.

In the medical plan alone, you must consider health plan design, the PBM (pharmacy benefit manager), stop loss coverage, network discounts, and medical management. Then there can be gym memberships, car and phone allowances, and even pet insurance. All of these affect your bottom line, so this begs the questions, "Why are you, the CEO, **not** the point of contact? Shouldn't **you** be the one to make decisions on the financial strategies of your company?"

Going beyond the financials, the right benefits package can be the key to acquiring (and retaining) the A-team talent you need to grow your business. You might ask yourself, "What is the cost of inaction?" And that answer could very well mean the difference between a weakening bottom line and a healthy, forward propelling company.

According to a recent article cited by SHRM (Society for HR Management), a major function of human resources is to provide _information_ regarding the various types of employee benefits. Among other things, these include: leaves of absence, employee assistance programs, and worker's compensation benefits. The actual benefit to the employee depends on how well the employee uses it. One of the biggest mistakes I see being made by leadership is being absent from the actual process and financial management conversations.

The financial health of your company and its employees should _**only**_ be tackled by the C-suite.

Think about it. Do you really think an employee who deeply cares for your team can make the hard decisions about money over people? They can't. Therefore, it's imperative you start the process yourself and turn it over to HR once the financial decisions, coverage design, pharmacy, and network side is complete.

Don't get me wrong. HR professionals are exceptionally good at helping people, and it's what they love to do. They should be involved, but not until it comes time to educate your employees on what's being offered, and not a minute sooner.

When you hand your HR department a high-quality healthcare plan that saves your employees both in premiums and healthcare costs, you have a winning combination. But if you hand that decision off and bury your head in the sand, all of that goes out the window.

Now that you understand the importance of being a part of the employee benefits decision, let's explore three major negative costs associated with not being as involved as you should be:

Employee Turnover

What is the cost of employee turnover? What's the cost of losing an employee who thinks they can find better benefits because they don't understand the benefits they currently have? How much money do you save if you retain that employee? It can be hard to calculate these costs, but they can be seen if you look hard enough.

In today's economy an organization needs to find and retain an A-Team if they are going to thrive and not just survive. Benefits play a huge role in this. Employees want quality benefits that make sense to them and fit the needs of their families, but because there are so many benefits to choose from it can be overwhelming. The best place to start is by focusing on the benefits your employees want the most and then offering those benefits with quality plans.

How do you know which benefits are of the greatest value to your employees? According to SHRM (Society of HR Managers), employees rank these benefits as extremely important: Health, dental, and vision insurance (88%), flexible hours (88%), vacation time (80%), and work from home options (80%). These are affordable and easy to understand. But unfortunately, the C-suite is usually so disconnected from this aspect of the business that they miss a golden opportunity to eliminate the high cost of employee turnover.

We all know happy employees help a business thrive and grow. Conversely, frequent turnover has the opposite effect. It begins with lowered employee morale, followed by a loss of productivity, and ultimately the company revenue suffers.

According to a study from the Work Institute, a shocking 42 million US employees left their jobs voluntarily in 2019 — this equates to 27 percent of the workforce. This is two million more than in 2018. Keep in mind this was <u>before</u> the turmoil caused by COVID-19.

Some studies project it costs, on average, 6 to 9 months' salary every time a business replaces a salaried employee. This equates to between $30,000 and $45,000 in recruiting and training expenses to replace a manager making $60,000 a year. The cost to replace a $10/hour retail employee would be $3,328. This is still too much to ignore no matter the size of the company.

In an insightful article on employee retention, Josh Bersin of Bersin by Deloitte breaks down key factors that contribute to the hard costs of losing an employee. These factors include:

- The cost of hiring a new employee, including advertising, interviewing, and screening

- The cost of onboarding a new person, including training and management time
- Lost productivity — it may take a new employee one to two years to reach the productivity of an existing employee
- Lost engagement — other employees who see high turnover tend to disengage and lose productivity
- Customer service and errors — new employees are slower and are often less adept at solving problems
- Training costs — over a two-to-three year span, a business is likely to invest 10 to 20 percent or more of an employee's salary in training.

The real cost of employee turnover is unknown because most companies don't have systems in place to track the costs of recruiting, interviewing, hiring, orientation and training, lost productivity, potential customer dissatisfaction, reduced or lost business, administrative costs, and lost expertise. All of this takes collaboration among various departments, including HR, Finance, Operations, and full oversight from the C-suite.

While the exact cost of employee turnover varies from industry to industry, the need to spend significant amounts of time and money to recruit and train new employees is universal. There's no question this is something employers, more specifically CEO/CFO's, need to manage.

Improving the benefits your company offers can play a major role in reducing your employee turnover and the associated costs. Above all else, your employees want to feel appreciated. The right benefit package can accomplish this goal. At the very least, better benefits can cause your employees to stop and think twice before leaving.

Strategic Control

What does it cost you when you give up strategic control over a critical investment? This expense is much bigger than you might think. The unknown costs associated with the health plan combined with all the other benefits you could offer is mind boggling.

Most of the players in this arena hide the "double dipping" taking place. Until you talk to the right person, you can't even know what those costs are. A good example of this is the double (and sometimes triple!) paybacks often buried in most pharmacy benefit plans. This is just one of the many unknown hidden costs in a very complex purchase.

You might think of this as *just* insurance, and just another expense. But to your employees, this is a safety net for their financial health. It's common to discuss hidden hard costs because those are easy to quantify, but there are also the intangible costs of sick and dying people to consider.

According to the ***Leapfrog Group*** (an organization responsible for grading hospitals), it's estimated thousands of patients are harmed and approximately 500 die every day in the U.S. from preventable problems such as medical error and infection. This inflates the healthcare cost to the employer by at least one third.

When it comes to hospitals, employers pay the price in more ways than one, beginning with which hospital to use. An upwards of 200,000 people die annually due to preventable hospital errors. Beyond the harm and suffering of your employees, employers and other purchasers pay an average of over $7,500 per hospital admission for errors, injuries, accidents, and infection.

In a new study by the ***John Hopkins Armstrong Institute for Private Safety and Quality***, hospitals graded D and F by Leapfrog were found to carry nearly twice the risk of mortality over A graded hospitals. Over 50,000 lives could be saved annually if all hospitals performed at the level of A grade facilities.

Do the "in network" hospitals that are on your medical plan have an A grade or not? The insurance companies know the answer, but because they are bound by contracts, they cannot and will not tell you. However, knowing the safety level of a hospital before you send your employees and their families there can save you thousands of dollars. At the bare minimum, don't you think you owe it to the people who are helping you build your business to find the highest quality healthcare providers you can?

This is <u>just one</u> of the hidden costs you don't know about lurking in the dark. Are you using an unbundled TPA (Third Party Administrator) and a transparent PBM (pharmacy benefits manager)? Do you have direct contracts with an A graded hospital? Is your stop loss policy concurrent with your plan document? Are you paying more than you should in administration fees? Are you using reference-based pricing? Most importantly, does your HR department know the answers to all these questions so they can educate your team on how to use the benefits you provide?

If you can't answer these high dollar questions, chances are you are paying too much for your benefits. So you can see how the convenience of passing the baton down the hall to HR and choosing not to know what's going on can result in an expensive (and avoidable) financial loss.

Taking part in the benefits decisions also speaks to your integrity as a leader. When you do so, it shows that you, as the CEO of your business, are doing all you can to take care of your people and lead them out of the fire.

Litigation and Liability

Probably the scariest cost associated with being absent from the benefits decision process is the potential for excessively large errors that could land you in a room with your legal team. Above and beyond all the other considerations, it's critical you know whether or not you're in legal compliance with your employee benefits.

There are at least three federal departments you're dealing with at any given time: Health and Human Services, the Department of Labor, and the IRS. These departments and the agencies within them are watching with an eagle eye, and it only takes one mistake for the cash outlay to become massive.

Let's say the HR department selects the benefits to the best of their ability and with the limited information they have available. They unknowingly choose a health plan in which the employees are forced to go to a D or F grade hospital, and the employee dies. Can your business be sued? The answer is a loud and emphatic "YES!"

You could easily find yourself defending your company in a civil lawsuit filed by the family of the deceased, stating you are at fault because you picked the plan they had to use.

In actuality, **you** didn't select the plan, but you did pass the buck to HR. Since HR was working under your direction, the fiduciary responsibility is legally still yours. This is probably the biggest reason you should always be involved in every conversation and decision concerning company benefits.

The federal government does not favor or discriminate against anyone when dishing out fines. Nor do they look the other way. (See the chapter by Jen Berman, on Fiduciary Responsibility for a more enlightening view on this topic.)

Now do you see why planning an employee benefit package should be a top-down strategy and not the other way around? If you care about your bottom line, like every CEO should, the potential costs are way too high to do it any other way.

HR is best at making people feel loved and appreciated. With the right tools, they can do this with excellence. You, as the CEO, are the best one to protect, strategize, and run all areas of the business.

When you expect HR to understand the ins and outs of the business AND respect the company money as if it's their own, it's like expecting cows to pick the best buyer for their milk. It's just not going to happen.

The C-suite should be giving HR a high-quality benefits package to protect the employee from financial hardships. Then, and only then, can HR present it and keep your employees happy and engaged.

Being an ostrich and sticking your head in the sand because you are too busy to do this is an easy excuse. What's not so easy is the hard financial reality you could face as a result of making that excuse. So which one are you? An ostrich or a CEO?

Tammera Hollerich

CEO, Mirus3 Inc.

As CEO of Mirus3 Inc., the parent company for IBT Consulting, Healthy Lifestyle Secrets, and Affairs Afloat Balloons, Tammera Hollerich is the icon of entrepreneurship as she has rolled a lifetime of accomplishments into a thriving profitable trio of companies.

In 1996, IBT Consulting, an all-female employee benefits firm, was created as an alternative to the then typical all male world of insurance. As a pioneer in the benefits industry, Tammera has earned some of the industry's highest awards. The one she is most proud of is being awarded Female Benefit Advisor of the Year in 2019.

After establishing IBT Consulting, it became apparent employers were in desperate need of a way to keep their employees healthy. In an effort to reduce the overall healthcare spend for her clients, she took on the challenge and created Healthy Lifestyle Secrets (HLS). HLS is a curriculum-based wellness and weight management program. It was originally developed as a value-added service to the consulting clients, but now stands on its own as a leader in nutritional education.

Rounding out the trio of companies is Affairs Afloat Balloons. This creative outlet quickly developed into an innovative and creative balloon design service for consumers and businesses throughout north Texas.

As a licensed insurance counselor, nutritionist, and nationally certified balloon artist, Tammera has created three consumer-centric companies that strive to provide extraordinary excellence each and every day.

Tammera is married, has a daughter, and seven dogs. They all happily reside in Fort Worth, Texas, where Mirus3 is headquartered.

CONTACT INFO

Connect with Tammera on LinkedIn at:
https://www.linkedin.com/in/tammerahollerich/
1-800-655-3363 | Tammera@ConsultIBT.com | www.Mirus3.com
8900 White Settlement Rd., Fort Worth, TX 76108

6

The Unlikely Guardians of American Healthcare

by Jennifer Berman, Esq.

A N EMPLOYER PLAN SPONSOR IS ALWAYS a fiduciary. It does not matter if the plan is fully insured or self funded.[1] It does not matter if the employer hires "world class" advisors. It does not matter if the employer outsources claims administration as almost all do. It does not matter if the chief executive officer has never engaged in a single conversation about the plan itself. No matter what, every single time, the plan sponsor—and yes, by proxy—the appropriate corporate executives, are fiduciaries. So, what exactly does it mean to be a fiduciary and how does this special responsibility play out in the context of an employer sponsored plan?

Equally as important, what does it really mean to act as a fiduciary in the health plan context? This chapter endeavors to not only define fiduciary duty, but also to explore what it means to be a good fiduciary in the context of a health plan. Hint: it's not just about money.

---

1   There is an argument that an employer may not be a fiduciary of a fully insured plan if they do not exercise ANY authority under that plan. However, in practice this is virtually never the case because employers are at the very least involved in selecting service providers in this context.

Taking This Seriously

As a corporate executive you have lots of responsibilities. You are likely reading this book because you are concerned about the cost of healthcare—not to be scolded by some lawyer about your heightened legal duties. That's fair. Here's why you need to take this seriously.

- As a fiduciary, you have **personal** liability to the plan.[2]

- This responsibility cannot be legally disclaimed.[3]

- Fiduciaries can be held liable for damages caused to an individual participant.[4]

- The DOL can assess civil penalties against fiduciaries of up to 20 percent of the amount recovered (1) in a settlement agreement (resulting from a DOL investigation), or (2) through an adverse court decision.[5]

- In the health plan context, your decisions can directly impact the health and wellbeing of your employees and their families.[6]

Defining Fiduciary Duty

Fiduciary duty is a legal concept. In short, to be a fiduciary means to be in a position of trust to act on behalf of another person. As a fiduciary, there are heightened ethical and legal expectations that you, the fiduciary, will put your best interests aside and instead act

---

2   See ERISA Section 409 providing that a breaching fiduciary is personally liable to "make good to such plan any losses to the plan resulting from each such breach, and to restore to such plan any profits of such fiduciary which have been made through use of assets of the plan by the fiduciary, and shall be subject to such other equitable or remedial relief as the court may deem appropriate, including removal of such fiduciary".

3   See ERISA Section 410(a) stating "any provision in an agreement or instrument which purports to relieve a fiduciary from responsibility or liability for any responsibility, obligation, or duty under this part shall be void as against public policy." The good news is you are permitted to buy insurance. ERISA Section 410(b).

4   ERISA Section 502(a)(3). See also CIGNA Corp. v. Amara, 131 S. Ct. 1866, 2011 WL 1832824 (2011).

5   ERISA Section 502(l).

6

in the best interest of another. Common examples of fiduciaries abound in modern society—think real estate agents, financial advisors, lawyers, doctors, and of course, executives in relationship to their shareholders.

Perhaps less obvious, but not less true, an employer stands in the shoes of its employees when making many of the decisions related to maintaining an employee benefit plan. Most employee benefit plans are governed by the Employee Retirement Income Security Act of 1974 (ERISA). Despite the reference to retirement in the name of the statute, ERISA is equally applicable to employer sponsored health plans—and in fact, there are a long line of successor statutes that apply to health plans (but not retirement plans) in this context including COBRA, HIPAA and the Affordable Care Act.

ERISA itself sets out the roadmap for being a good plan fiduciary providing as follows:

> *[A] fiduciary shall discharge his duties with respect to the plan solely in the interest of the participants and beneficiaries and—*
>
> *(A) For the exclusive purpose of:*
>
> > *(i) Providing benefits to participants and their beneficiaries; and*
> >
> > *(ii) defraying reasonable expenses of administering the plan;*
>
> *(B) with the care, skill, prudence, and diligence under the circumstances then prevailing that a prudent man acting in a like capacity and familiar with such matters would use in the conduct of an enterprise of a like character and with like aims;*
>
> *(C) by diversifying the investments of the plan so as to minimize the risk of large losses, unless under the circumstances it is clearly prudent not to do so; and*

> (D) *in accordance with the documents and instruments governing the plan...*[7]

From this statutory language, four key rules for plan sponsors emerge:

- Rule # 1: Always act **exclusively** in the best interest of the individuals covered under your health plan.

- Rule # 2: You are expected to understand how health plans work, and **act like it**.

- Rule #3: It's **not your money**, take care of it wisely.

- Rule #4: Your plan document is the **contract**—follow it.

With these rules in mind, we can begin our exploration of what it really means to be a fiduciary in the context of an employer sponsored health plan.

What's Not Covered

If, at this point, you are scratching your head in abject confusion and wondering how on earth every decision you make relative to a health plan can be done in the "best interest" of your employees, that confusion is warranted. It's worth taking a moment to review those elements of maintaining a health plan that are NOT covered by the fiduciary duty rules. On this, we are luckily aided by the U.S. Department of Labor. In its fiduciary duty guide, the DOL expressly provides that certain business decisions are not made in a fiduciary capacity. These include:

- Establishing a plan,

- Determining the benefit package,

- Including certain features in a plan,

---

7   ERISA Section 404.

- Amending a plan, and
- Terminating a plan.[8]

These decisions are generally known as "settlor" functions. When making these determinations, employers are permitted to consider their own best interests and make decisions based on such considerations. However, once the plan is established, fiduciary duties attach.

Money Matters, But It's Not the Only Thing That Does

The requirement to monitor plan expenses is a traditional focus of compliance efforts surrounding fiduciary duties. Substantial regulatory regimes have arisen in both the retirement and health plan context to ensure that fiduciaries have the appropriate information to make sound financial decisions on behalf of their plans. These transparency rules are largely designed to allow fiduciaries to ensure that they are spending plan funds wisely. How can you ensure compensation is reasonable without knowing what it is?

While much time and attention has been spent on the issue of compensation, fiduciaries are required to think more broadly. Money matters, but **quality** matters too. In selecting service providers, fiduciaries are **NOT** required to select the lowest cost option. In fact, fiduciaries are required to "engage in an objective process designed to elicit information necessary to assess the qualifications of the provider, the quality of the services offered, and the reasonableness of the fees charged in light of the services provided."[9] Thus, your job is to measure **value**.

---

8   "Understanding Your Fiduciary Responsibilities Under a Group Health Plan," U.S. Department of Labor, 2019, pg. 2.
9   DOL Information Letter to Diana Orantes Ceresi, 1998 WL 1638068 (Feb. 19, 1998).

Decisions, Decisions...

So, how exactly are you supposed to make a good decision in this context? The first step is making sure you have good options. You can't just assume that the insurance carrier or network with the biggest name is the best and sign on the bottom line. Nor can you just pick the cheapest option on the market. The law (and basic prudence) require a real investigation into the options available.

In evaluating these options, the DOL directs fiduciaries to:

(1) Compare firms based on the same information.
Pick your metrics and stick to them. These can include services offered, experience, cost, quality assessments, etc. Don't forget to also consider a firm's financial condition and its experience with health plans like yours.

(2) Evaluate quality.
Quality comes in many shapes and sizes. Factors you should consider include:
- The identity, experience, and qualifications of the professionals who will be handling the plan or providing medical services.
- Any recent litigation or enforcement action taken against the service provider.
- The service provider's experience and performance record.
- Ease of access to medical providers and information about the healthcare provider's operations.
- The procedures in place to timely consider and resolve patient questions and complaints.

- The procedures for patient record confidentiality.
- The methodology used to ensure that any required licenses, ratings or accreditations are up to date. [10]

It's also not enough to just think about these issues. Really, even evaluating them in depth isn't enough. In the legal world, it's not real until it's documented. It is therefore critical that you document your evaluation process. This doesn't necessarily mean you need to run a full request for proposal every time you hire a vendor. But it does mean you need to engage in a **process,** and you need to maintain records of that process.

Once you make your decision, you aren't quite done. You also need to make sure that your relationship with your vendor is codified. Yes, you need a contract—preferably before services commence. The DOL states this point clearly and succinctly: "Read, understand, and keep copies of all contracts."[11] If you read these words and can't help but think, "I'd rather stick needles in my eyeballs"— you aren't alone. There is nothing preventing you from getting help. In fact, there are scores of healthcare advisors, consultants, attorneys, etc. who actually like this stuff. Find them, engage them, take them to dinner, send wine — they've got your back, but only if you let them help.

The Moral Imperative

As noted at the outset, conversations about fiduciary duty in the context of ERISA are mainly about money. This is, of course, because retirement plans are basically all about money. It is also because the roots of ERISA's fiduciary regime can be found in the traditional common law around trusts and estates—again, all about money.

---

10   "Understanding Your Fiduciary Responsibilities Under a Group Health Plan," U.S. Department of Labor, 2019, pg. 5.
11   Id.

But in the health plan context, the decisions made by fiduciaries are about much more than money. Sure, self-pay is always an "option"—but, the reality is that health plans serve as the gatekeepers to medical care in our system.

This leaves business leaders in a position of responsibility they may never have chosen for themselves. But, the reality is that over 55 percent of Americans are covered through employer provided health insurance.[12] As such, thousands of business leaders find themselves in the position of having to make decisions that can literally mean the difference between life and death for employees and their loved ones. You likely didn't sign up for this. But consider for a moment the possibility that you are precisely the right person to hold this responsibility. Our health system is exceedingly complex. The average American accesses it at precisely the moment in which they are most vulnerable. Physicians and providers need to focus on helping all of us stay well. So, who better to serve as the guardian of the system than American business leaders?

As an executive, you are trained to navigate complexity. Sure, unless you are in the healthcare industry, you likely didn't expect that complexity to include responsibility for people's health. But the ask isn't for you to become a physician—or even to understand complex medical terminology. The ask is that you use your business skills to make sure the vendors you select to run your health plans take care of your employees and their families in multiple dimensions: by controlling costs and quality, thus creating true value.

---

12   "Health Insurance Coverage in the United States: 2019," U.S. Census Bureau, September 2020.

Jennifer Berman, Esq.

CEO
MZQ Consulting

JEN BERMAN is an employee benefits attorney and entrepreneur. She is a leader in analyzing healthcare reform developments and frequently serves as a speaker and commentator on a wide variety of healthcare reform and employee benefits issues. In addition to her work leading MZQ, she is a member of Holder Law Group LLC. Jen graduated cum laude from the University of Pennsylvania Law School, where she was Editor-in-Chief of the University of Pennsylvania Journal of Labor and Employment Law. Jen also completed her undergraduate studies at the University of Pennsylvania, graduating magna cum laude. She is an avid lover of textile arts, frequently wearing stunning pieces she hand-crafted herself.

CONTACT INFO ———————————————————————————

    (443)-948-6800
    engage@mzqconsulting.com
    www.mzqconsulting.com

7

Successful Change Management on Your Benefits Journey

by Marc Wilson

FOR YEARS, THE COST AND QUALITY of benefits has been a problem for business owners and employees alike, and it's only getting worse. The status-quo benefits system causes employers to waste tens or even hundreds of thousands of dollars per year, all while delivering their valued workers a level of care that is, at best, mediocre.

There's no question that the way we look at benefits is overdue for an overhaul, and many benefits advisers are scrambling to take business owners from a problem to a solution as fast as possible. In the rush to improve their clients' benefits plans, though, they often forget the most critical part of the process: the implementation.

Big problems (or big opportunities) can't be addressed with the flip of a switch. The reality is that the journey to better benefits is less like a bridge from point A to point B and more like a vast ocean of possibilities and challenges. This gap between your starting point and your destination is where the real success of your journey is found, and yet, it's often the part that many business owners overlook.

A benefits plan that puts your employees first is, of course, a "finish line" that every employer should strive for. Even great benefits plans, however, often fail because leaders and employees aren't considered or incorporated into the changes taking place. Business owners set sail with just a compass, not understanding that a detailed map and a crew comprised of an educated, engaged team is what will carry them safely and comfortably over even the choppiest waters.

Your adviser can serve as your guide on your path to better benefits, not only mapping out the path from start to finish, but also keeping your employees informed about where they're going, how they're getting there, and what they may see and experience along the way.

A Plan for Change

The best benefits advisers don't just offer a solution — they also offer a change management plan to help make the transition smooth and easy to understand. Your employees are likely accustomed to a broken healthcare system that puts big insurance companies' interests first. Still, even when workers have been assured that a system that serves *them* is on the horizon, the introduction of new tools and strategies can be intimidating if they don't understand how to use them.

Your adviser's job isn't just to align vendors with clients, but also to help you and your employees navigate the healthcare system. A great adviser is in the business of taking care of people from start to finish and beyond, and they'll understand that the end product will yield far better results if *everyone* involved is comfortable and knowledgeable throughout the journey.

Part of your adviser's job should always be ***change management***, or planning and facilitating a successful transition to the solutions that lead to improved healthcare plans. The importance of excellent change management cannot be overstated. When neglected or executed poorly, the result is frustrated employees which can lead to a frustrated HR department, which can then radiate throughout the business and complicate day-to-day business.

Proper and careful change management, however, can supercharge the transition from problems to solutions without causing additional issues along the way. For this to be successful, three crucial steps must take place in your adviser's change management plan.

1. Engaging the Rational Mind

Any decent adviser will be able to provide concrete, comprehensive reasons for you and your employees to get on board with a new and improved benefits plan. Engaging the ***rational mind*** is arguably the easiest step in making your employees more comfortable with the forthcoming changes.

This step involves showing your employees measurable, irrefutable results through data and calculations. In the benefits world, your adviser may engage the rational side of your employees' minds by:

- Calculating potential savings
- Breaking down the change process into measurable steps
- Sharing case studies from other businesses that have made similar changes

For example, let's say you have an employee who requires shoulder surgery. You learn that if they go to a hospital ten minutes from home for the procedure, the operation will cost about $43,000. However, if they're willing to drive to an outpatient surgery center forty minutes from home, the cost of the surgery will be cut to just $10,000. Providing your employee with numbers like this can give them hard evidence that, although this change may be intimidating, it will save a substantial amount of money.

Make no mistake — engaging the rational mind is crucial to getting your employees to engage with your new benefits plan. Just as we'd want our guide to explain the various steps to get from point A to point B on our trip, your employees will feel reassured when they understand the evidence and concrete facts about their new and improved benefits plan.

Still, the rational mind is the shallowest layer to crack in your change management plan. Your employees can have all the numbers and explanations laid out for them on paper, but until they understand the bigger picture and what it truly means for them, your company's benefits plan will likely continue to be another confusing and cumbersome problem to navigate throughout their employment. In fact, if the emotional mind isn't engaged, as well, your new and improved benefits plan may feel about the same to your employees as your old, outdated one.

2. Engaging the Emotional Mind

Once your employees know *what* their new benefits plan will do for them, they need to understand *how* these changes will impact their lives for the better. This involves engaging their **emotional mind** to help them see the more profound results of high-value benefits.

Let's return to the employee who is getting ready to have shoulder surgery. Simple math may tell them that getting the operation done at the outpatient center will cost significantly less than getting it done at the hospital. Until they understand what this means for *them*, however, the prospect of driving an extra thirty minutes may still not be worth the inconvenience for them, especially when getting similar procedures done at the hospital was the norm under their previous benefits plan.

Thankfully, there are myriad opportunities to engage your employee's emotional mind in this situation. For example, you could offer your employee a $3,000 bonus for choosing the outpatient center, providing them with a substantial financial reward while still saving $7,000 yourself. This is a short-term incentive that could provide your employee with any number of long-term rewards, whether they want to pay off debt, go on vacation, or boost their children's college fund.

Financial incentives aren't the only way to tap into your employees' emotions when it comes to changes in their benefits plan. Your adviser can also discuss your employee's options with them, one-on-one, to show them how a surgery center that specializes in their required procedure could offer them better care, leading to faster recovery and fewer complications down the road.

Suddenly, the decision to make the drive to the outpatient center doesn't just make sense — it *feels* right. The initial difficulty of adapting to a new process becomes worthwhile when your employees can see the rewards at the end. Soon enough, a journey that was once uncomfortable will become the new normal, and your employees' emotional connection to that process will help carry your whole team to the finish line.

Ensuring your employees' emotional engagement doesn't just impact the benefits side of your business, either. Status-quo benefits plans are often a major stressor for employees, with high costs hurting their finances and low-quality care impacting their physical health. Better benefits — and educated, engaged employees — can reduce absenteeism and turnover as your workforce becomes healthier and, yes, happier. That motivation will weave itself into the whole company, boosting employee morale and creating a workplace culture that current and prospective employees want to be a part of.

The rational mind can help your employees *accept* change, but the emotional mind is what *drives* change. When staff understand how their new plan will improve their lives, they themselves will be more eager to engage with their benefits. And a great benefits adviser will give them plenty of opportunities and reasons to do so.

3. Creating A Blueprint for Success

As your employees grow to understand and embrace their new benefits system, your adviser should be working with you and your C-suite to create a benefits blueprint. Change won't happen overnight, but you can facilitate the process step-by-step to create an environment in which change is possible.

This blueprint will serve as your company's map, and while your employees will look to you as their captain, this ship won't sail properly without a fully engaged crew. The internal leaders of your organization should be champions of your company's new benefits plan, taking the initiative to get involved and use the new tools and strategies available to them. On this journey, if anyone works alone, the rough seas will never get smoother.

The key to a successful change management blueprint is to break a large, comprehensive plan down into easily digestible pieces. While your efforts to engage the rational and emotional mind will show your employees *why* these changes are being made and *how* they'll affect your workers, your blueprint should explain the rest of the process, such as:

- *Who* and *what* is involved in each step
- *Where* each step is expected to occur on the change timeline
- *When* employees should expect to see the results

Employee education is crucial in the successful implementation of a new benefits plan. Status-quo plans may seem "easier" to employees at first, providing them with fewer options and a one-size-fits-all model, but the outcome is that your employees take a back seat in a benefits plan they can't understand or control.

A lack of employee education isn't just detrimental to the employees themselves. Confusion breeds frustration, and frustration leads to inaction. This inaction can completely derail all the hard work you've put into opening your employees' minds to the upcoming changes in their plan. If your employees are confused and frustrated and don't use the new solutions, your business will never reap the rewards of your new and improved benefits plan.

Providing transparency and clarity throughout the change process will make your employees more likely to use the new tools provided by your adviser. Once your workers can see the path ahead and understand their role in the navigation, they'll be more likely to step into that role and become active participants in their benefits plan. Empowered, educated employees are far more likely to see the results they *should* get out of their plan, including:

- Improved quality of care
- Decreased costs
- Peace of mind

These key indicators of a successful plan are especially important when you consider how many of your employees' family members are also included in your company's plan. Change management isn't just for your workers' comfort — it's also for the health and security of their children and spouses.

A great adviser will implement educational strategies into your benefits plan to productively engage your employees throughout the change process and beyond. Group and one-on-one meetings can provide staff with the opportunity to ask questions in a comfortable environment, while technology-based tools can put information and educational resources at your employee's fingertips. When accessibility is prioritized in your benefits plan, your employees will seize the educational opportunities presented to them.

The Impact of Little Victories

Even with a step-by-step blueprint and engagement of both the rational and emotional mind, winning over your employees with your new benefits plan can be a hard-fought battle in the beginning. This process becomes easier, however, if the beginning focuses on small wins rather than a distant promise of grand, sweeping change.

The benefits industry has remained largely unchanged for years, and despite its ineffectiveness, its consistency keeps its customers complacent. Employees know what to expect from the status-quo benefits system, even if it doesn't deliver the results they want or deserve. They may not *like* paying more and more and more every year for benefits that constantly decrease in quality, but the idea of change can be so uncomfortable that even the prospect of something *better* may be unappealing if the premise is vastly different than what they're used to.

In other words, the first step of your journey isn't overcoming the waves; it's moving your ship from the shore into the sea.

One of the easiest places to achieve the small wins needed to open your employees' minds to the possibility of change is through your pharmacy program. Pharmacy spends are relatively simple changes, as you can often deliver the exact same medications — brand names and all — more efficiently and at a lower cost.

Consider how hands-on the prescription process is for your employees: they go to the doctor, get their prescription, then go to the pharmacy and pay for their medication. This is such a familiar process for so many people that the effects of change are tangible and easy to recognize. Think about how their experience might change if:

- They didn't have to see their doctor in-person to refill their prescription
- The cost of their medication drastically decreased
- Their medication was delivered to them

A relatively small, widely applicable change like this one can spark a far-reaching change in mindset throughout your entire business. This satisfies the rational mind by creating a measurable decrease in both money and time spent acquiring the medication, while the emotional mind is engaged by the convenience and relief presented by the new process. The more opportunities you can find to give your employees a taste of how their new plan can help them, the more enthusiastic they'll be to embrace change when it presents itself in larger forms.

Smooth Sailing

Change of any kind can be intimidating at best and terrifying at worst. Your company's benefits plan directly and profoundly impacts your employees, which is why their comfort and understanding should be the driving force behind your change management plan.

When crafting the perfect solution to your business' benefits dilemma, remember that success depends on your implementation being as careful and thought-out as the plan itself. Developing a next-generation benefits plan involves big changes for your employees and the company, which is why your change process must be broken down into smaller, critical steps.

By engaging the rational and emotional mind of your employees, you can help open their minds to a process of change that will ultimately yield high-quality, low-cost results. As you work with your adviser to create a benefits blueprint, this process is no longer an endless, intimidating ocean. Instead, it turns into a series of manageable waves. Best of all, no one is on this journey alone; a great adviser will involve everyone in your business, guaranteeing that the people impacted by the plan itself understand how to use it to their advantage.

The prospect of a complete and polished next-generation benefits plan is, of course, an admirable (and achievable) goal. But if you want the finished product to reach its full potential, you need to approach each small step with care, consideration, and compassion.

When your employees are prepared to face each wave, it's much harder to rock the boat.

Marc Wilson

CEO
The Wesmarc Group

MARC WILSON'S passion is to positively impact the health and wealth of organizations and their employees. Marc has over 14 years of experience working in the employee benefits industry. He believes that there is a better way for employers to deliver high-quality healthcare at a lower cost to their employees. He launched The Wesmarc Group after realizing that the traditional health insurance model with misaligned incentives was contributing to the problem in our healthcare system.

The Wesmarc Group is a transparent fee-based consulting firm that helps organizations retake control and reclaim precious capital so that they can reinvest in their company, people, corporate social responsibility or cause. The Wesmarc Group identifies unrecognized financial opportunities that are "trapped" inside operating expenses as excess funding or over insuring and then help you manage risk, recover millions, free up cash flow, and show you how to invest in your organization's healthcare system so that your employees will have more access to higher quality care at lower costs while increasing your bottom line.

CONTACT INFO

(480)-707-8182
marc@refreshmybenefits.com

8

Mission-Driven Benefits

by Ben Conner

IT HAS BEEN AN INTERESTING eight years as the leader of Conner Insurance. I became CEO of our family business in 2013 at the age of 29. I attribute this early and significant success to being hired by some of Indiana's largest, most well-recognized companies to consult on their employee benefits program. As I embarked on my business leadership journey, I drew from the experiences of other business executives and my time as a basketball coach at my alma mater high school. I observed that every leader put their personal touch on their business or team to drive outcomes and build culture. So, when I become CEO, I was ready to do the same.

I was ready to create a culture where we build strong relationships with co-workers and clients, and we were having FUN in the process. My vision was to go for a tech-company feel with ping-pong tables in the breakroom. We would work hard and enjoy the journey. Sounds like a plan, right? It turns out, something was missing from that vision, and that was the mission and accountability around how business is done.

I must admit it took me more than a year to overcome that improper focus for building our company, and it would take the next three years to slow down, readjust and launch ourselves into the plan of what we wanted to accomplish in business and life. We restructured our team, changed our practices, and built the accountability missing from a mission-driven company. That's when we decided to recast our mission and foundational values. Our mission is to build relationships, solve problems, serve people, and pursue excellence. Our foundational values can be summarized by having integrity, being accountable, innovative, and kind.

Now, we have a collective drive pulling in the same direction. We have a group of individuals committed to putting their best work forward toward the collective effort of team success. We are mission-driven.

We have seen the fruit of our labor by earning Indiana Best Places to Work nominations for multiple years, as well as Indiana Healthiest Employer nominations. One of the best outcomes we've seen from building this culture is that the leadership team is not alone in managing and protecting it. Our entire Conner Insurance Family is protective of our culture and the individuals who get to be a part of it. This protection allows for the continual building of high-performing teams with high expectations. This has all been the outcome of being mission-driven in instilling baseline principles into every area of our business.

Author Trey Taylor says it concisely in his book *A CEO Does Three Things*, where he suggests that the entire job of a CEO can be summed up in three words, "People. Culture. Numbers." I agree with Taylor and believe the true job of a CEO is to build a team driven to move the business forward, develop a culture where employees can be fulfilled and accomplish meaningful work, and run a financially successful business that is a stable workplace for employees.

The reality is that being successful in all these areas means that we need to be mission-driven in the details. Without that key differentiator, we only have transactional experiences with people and numbers. With a mission-driven cultural approach, we can create an experience where people want to work to drive meaningful change and create an experience for customers and co-workers that is transformational to a business.

You may wonder, "what does this have to do with employee benefits or the process of partnering with my employee benefits advisor?" I would suggest that it has everything to do with benefits and the right advisor. I have met with hundreds of employers and listened to their stories about their businesses. These leaders talk about the foundation of their business and the vision for the future. They talk about their workforce and how much they care for them. At some point, we get to the conversation of employee benefits and the programs and plans they have in place. They often explain their programs and are indifferent about the offerings. What I find is that their business and culture strategies aren't reflected in their benefits strategy.

Other times we have employers who are embarrassed or ashamed of the offerings for their employees. I hear more often than not that an employee benefits program is disconnected from the mission-driven culture these business leaders have worked tirelessly to build. The approach is disconnected at best, and at worst, is ultimately working against the employer. For the most part, these business leaders are building a culture that is an immersive experience for their workforce. These leaders want to be holistic in engaging with their employees and help balance the work/life equation. An incredible amount of work and thought goes into creating this experience, but unfortunately, their benefits program has been transactional.

It doesn't have to be this way. A business leader can make the same careful considerations in an employee benefits program as they do in all the other business units within your overall business. Even more importantly, employee benefits programs shouldn't work against the efforts and gains made in other areas. The reality is benefits are a complimentary component of total compensation. Whatever is spent in the benefits realm, these funds are diverted away from the direct compensation to your workforce.

So how do businesses connect their overall mission and values with their delivery of benefits to their employees? How do businesses create a benefits deliverable that is not disjointed from their people, culture, and numbers strategy? There are three simple steps to align the mission of your business to the delivery of Mission-Driven Benefits.

Step one: Set the Solid Foundation

I learned from my mistakes early in my business leadership journey. One thing that I learned is that a solid foundation matters. On the surface, I thought "fun" was what I wanted in business, but it indeed wasn't. If I had dug deep enough, I would have discovered that what I needed was to win the right way. I would have found that I needed to grow our business by working hard and engaging our customers and prospects with integrity. I would realize that the best way to get there is to work hard and focus on the details.

In my basketball experience, I also learned through playing and coaching that "fun" was not the focus either. If we focused on just "fun," it never came to fruition. I assure you clowning around with friends and losing was not "fun." I quickly learned that "fun" in sports was working hard and going through the process of becoming a better player and team, which ultimately led to winning. If only I had taken that lesson and applied it to business earlier.

As a business leader, to have success in building a mission-driven benefits program, you must already have a solid mission and company values. It would be impossible as a leadership team to create a program that aligns with your business's mission or foundational values if these things have not been set or if you cannot clearly articulate them.

When there is not a solid foundation for a business's mission and values, there is too much room for interpretation or focusing on the wrong things with little importance. Without a complete perspective of the mission and vision, compensation and benefits can turn into a transactional relationship, a zero-sum game versus a strategic opportunity to grow people and culture within your business.

To succeed in creating a mission-driven approach to benefits, you must be a mission-driven business.

Step two: Build the Right Team

Most companies need to maintain a complementary strategy to build the right teams internally and externally.

It doesn't matter what business you are in; growth and success are tied to hiring the right people that have the right expertise to complete the job the right way. Companies are only as good as the talent to which they can attract and grow. Therefore, selecting the right talent in any organization is critical to growth and success.

However, selecting the right talent is not enough. In 2014 when we began restructuring our internal team, we needed to hold our current team accountable to the mission and foundational values that we set and then recruit talent that fit them. One of the keys to our current success is building a culture where everyone is accountable for themselves transparently. We include our teams in the process. I have heard it said that "people will show up for their job, but they will die for a cause." I believe this is what makes a good team great. They are not only the right individuals to accomplish a task together as a team, but they are committed to the mission of what they are doing and why they are doing it.

The same approach applies to selecting the right external partners, specifically your employee benefits advisor. However, it is transferable to other external partners in your business (accountant, attorney, commercial insurance consultant, marketing professional, etc.). Employee benefits is a complex environment, which is why Benefits Advisors and Brokers exist. The job of external partners is to give the appropriate guidance to navigate the landscape of their area of expertise and apply the trends and strategies to your business.

Here are a few characteristics to look for when selecting the right Employee Benefits Advisor:

- Do they consult from a position where they keep your workforce in mind?

- Are they deeply involved with establishing trends in the employee benefits space?

- Do they understand how healthcare financing works and how that impacts you?

- Do they have a vision for navigating long-term / short-term business strategies related to employee benefits?

- Do they have a proven game plan?

When building your external partnerships, it is vital to keep the same standards as you would when building your internal team.

There needs to be alignment with the individual or partner and the needs of your business. Still, ultimately, they need to be mission-aligned to get your organization where it needs to go and to guide you on the path of how to get your business there.

To create a mission-driven approach to benefits, select the right internal and external talent that have the skills and ability to achieve short-term and long-term success.

Step three: Establish a Game Plan

Once an organization has established the mission and value approach, placed the right internal and external talent that is culturally aligned, it is time to develop the proper strategic game plan for the organization. The same logic around establishing a game plan for your business can be applied to your employee benefits program, which is a game plan that is constantly evolving. There are plenty of worthy books that discuss the strategy and process of establishing an appropriate business strategic game plan, so we will spend this segment discussing what that looks like in the employee benefits world. There are four things you need to ensure when beginning to establish an employee benefits game plan:

1. The Executive Leadership Team needs to be involved.
2. Create A SWOT analysis and monitor over time.
   This identifies your employee benefits program's strengths, weaknesses, opportunities, and threats.
3. Establish a multi-year plan and perform regular reviews and assessments.
4. Review for continuous improvement and make changes as needed.

The entire Executive Leadership Team should be involved in establishing the game plan because employee benefits are a complicated, emotional, and expensive compensation item. Remember, compensation and benefits are tied together. If benefits are removed, compensation can increase. If compensation needs to increase, the ability to invest in benefits would likely decrease. The table stakes are high for employee benefits, especially since it is your organization's second or third largest expense. For this reason, organizations need to treat it with that level of importance.

The employee benefits program can help an organization gain a significant competitive advantage in recruitment, retention, compensation, and bottom-line results. That is why it is imperative to build an appropriate SWOT analysis. The outcome of this analysis is where the business plan can be established or adjusted.

We identify risks and problems that our clients need to solve to meet their objectives through the swot analysis. As a result, we created our Conner Healthcare Spectrum to help our clients navigate their problems and solve their most pressing issues. Additionally, this allows employers to see important items on the horizon and helps them build a multi-year plan and adapt accordingly.

We know every employer is different, so where a business moves along the spectrum is highly customized. We also know that not all employers will want to adopt all items on the spectrum, so we will hand-select items that we believe are workable within their organization and culture. In addition, those items position them the best for recruiting, retention, compensation, and bottom-line results. Lastly, we know that the spectrum is ever-evolving because business is ever-evolving, so the spectrum as it exists today is as follows:

Conner Healthcare Spectrum

BASELINE	FUNDING	PHARMACY	RISK MANAGEMENT	EMPLOYEE ENGAGEMENT	MEDICAL CONTRACTING I	MEDICAL CONTRACTING II	EMPLOYEE WELLBEING
STAGE 1	STAGE 2	STAGE 3	STAGE 4	STAGE 5	STAGE 6	STAGE 7	STAGE 8
Fully Insured	Level Funded Self-Funded	Transparent PBM Rx Advocacy J-Code Management	Insurance Bulk Purchasing Post Payment Claims Forensics Plan Design Restructure Data Analytics	Cost & Quality Transparency Member Experience Coordinator Customized Communication Channels	Bundled Surgical Pricing Centers of Excellence Direct Hospital Contracting	Aggressive Medical Management with $0 deductible Reference Based Pricing	Advanced Biometrics Mission-Driven Wellness Mental Health Advocacy

OVERALL SAVINGS

0% | 5% | 10% | 15% | 20% | 35% | 40%

Using this spectrum as the blueprint or guide, employers can establish a workable game plan today and give a vision for the future.

Lastly, you need to review your strategy and game plan often, as we did in 2014. We recognized we were off course, our plan needed to be adjusted, and we needed to establish different objectives. In your business journey, you may be at that point as well. These are all active decisions and evaluations on where you want to take the program. The bottom line is that your plans need to support your mission.

To succeed in creating a mission-driven approach to benefits, strategically establishing and reviewing your game plan will drive competitive advantages in recruitment, retention, compensation, and bottom-line results.

Most of the time, leaders learn the best lessons from failure. As I explained earlier, I learned lessons the hard way by not setting the proper foundation, having the wrong team in place, and not establishing the appropriate game plan from the start. But, ultimately, failing isn't the failure. What I learned is success can come from failure if you can learn from it.

I am confident these three steps will help you build a successful mission-driven benefits program by leading and supporting your workforce in the short and long term. I have witnessed business leaders implement this strategy that drives results, transparent processes and allows them to stay focused on the most important things.

Ben Conner

CEO
Conner Insurance

After graduating with a degree in finance from Indiana Wesleyan University in 2006, Ben signed on with Conner Insurance as an insurance advisor. Using his strengths in strategic planning, finance, and communication, Ben's exceptional vision and execution with his clients led him to be recognized as a top advisor in both the firm and the US insurance industry.

Because of his outstanding efforts, Ben was promoted to CEO in 2013. In 2015, Ben Conner and his business partners acquired Conner Insurance from the previous owners. In the fifteen years since Ben's joining the firm, Conner Insurance has experienced substantial success retaining 90% of its clients, growing by three times and becoming one of Indiana's most trusted consulting firms. Utilizing his leadership, work ethic and expertise, Ben's benefits clients have experienced best in class national results in managing their health plans. Eighty percent of Ben's clients have experienced flat or reduced healthcare expenses over the last 5-10 years, which is unheard of in the benefits healthcare industry.

Through his guidance and focus on workplace culture, Conner Insurance has been one of the 100 Healthiest Workplaces in America. Conner Insurance was a Top 10 finalist for the Best Places to Work in Indiana in 2014, 2015, 2016, and 2020. Ben was recognized by BenefitsPro magazine as a finalist for the 2020 Broker of the Year award. He was also named a Rising Star in Advising in 2019 by Employee Benefit Adviser. Ben was also recognized in 2021 by the Indianapolis Business Journal as a 40 under 40 recipient.

Ben lives in Fishers, IN with his wife, Alyssa, and their three children. Ben loves to read, play/watch sports, travel, and spend time with his family.

CONTACT INFO

(317)-808-7711 | bhconner@connerins.com | www.connerins.com

9

The Relativity
of Risk

by Griffin Meredith

As you have undoubtedly determined from the title of this book, foreword, and surrounding chapters, the point of this collaboration is to draw attention to issues of cost and quality in healthcare and the inverted relationship that has now become widely accepted as an unyielding fact. This sector is perceived by most employers, employees, and the average American as different than any other due to the lack of transparency surrounding it, and everyone thinks this is a truth you must accept. However, this is simply not the case.

How the typical health insurance plan of the 21st century came to be is quite simple. After World War II ended and US employers were forced to offer additional benefits to attract and retain talent, they began to offer healthcare insurance as a perk. Over the years, that pool of benefits started to grow and went from just physician and hospital services to many more items, including prescriptions. As their administration became more complicated, intermediaries began finding ways to make it easier to manage for a slightly higher price. Over time, this sector of the economy ballooned, primarily due to these intermediaries, each protecting their interest with a lack of transparency and burying it within the health insurance premium. These self-protected interests created the problem of escalating prices in the healthcare sector. However, many employers, state governments, and associations have proactively managed the issues created by this dysfunctional system. Now these entities are reversing the course of letting an intermediary "make it easy" for them with a packaged premium, opting to unpack this riddle with solutions such as a Next-Generation Health Plan (or something similar). They correctly understand what they pay, to whom and where, and the value they are getting for each piece of their premium.

A common belief many Americans still hold about these traditional plans is that we need health insurance to protect us against catastrophic risk. While health insurance does protect you from possibly depleting your life savings, the reality is that there are many other components of what goes into your health insurance premium. Only a tiny portion of that elusive number truly protects you against significant financial risk. This "riddle, wrapped in a mystery, inside of an enigma," as Winston Churchill once said, is why truly understanding self-funding and the concepts of a Next-Generation Health Plan is a necessity for any business.

Let's address some of the common initial thoughts an executive has when hearing the term self-funding. It could range from, "We're not ready" or "We don't understand it" to "Couldn't one claim bankrupt us?" and so on. Ultimately, there is one conclusion nearly all C-level executives have in their thought process: "Self-funding sounds risky." While I understand that the term "self-funding" itself sounds less secure than "fully insured," this is a problem of terminology and not one of risk. For example, if you could place an order for lunch for eight people at a restaurant with eight different entrees, and these entrees cost $1.00 each if purchased individually or $10.00 for all eight ordered in advance, would you choose the latter? Of course not! If the most you would spend was $8.00 to consume every entrée when ordered separately, you would likely order each item at the one dollar price point. There is no reason to pay the extra two dollars since there is no increase in value to you. However, this happens in most companies across the United States every day with their healthcare expenses. With fully insured health plans, the belief is that you are buying a guarantee not to go above your risk tolerance. Yet, you can accomplish those same goals in a self-funded arrangement and with a tremendous upside, such as lower costs, transparency, and removing those middlemen.

We can easily follow along in the restaurant scenario because we understand the basic economics of not paying $10.00 for $8.00 of value. Herein lies the problem with many C-Level executives. They have probably dealt with this sector of their business and may think they understand it adequately, but they likely do not comprehend every nuance because there are so many details. So circling back to the issue of risk, as humans, we will usually only take the appropriate amount of risk when faced with hardships or problems we truly understand. Human nature directs us to take intelligent risks, but we fall back on doing what we think is playing it safe when there is a lack of understanding. Staying fully insured with your health insurance plan is not playing it safe at all. You are paying that extra $2.00 for no added value. Some of you may be thinking that being fully insured is convenient because neither you nor your staff need another item on your plates! (pun intended). That argument may have been understandable when a company with a small staff was spending $2000-$3000 per employee per year, which may have been the case with plans 15-20 years ago. But when the average fully insured family health plan across the US is now $28,256 (Milliman, 2021), employers are making costly mistakes by not taking the time to evaluate what they are doing with their health plan, or even what it is they are insuring against. Imagine that extra two dollars multiplied by tens of thousands of dollars each year.

In this chapter I am really just trying to convey that risk is relative, and you should understand that you are not insuring against the visit to your family physician or that trip to the urgent care center for a child's sprained ankle. Few would argue that paying more than $2,300 per month for family health insurance is worth it because one year when the kids were little you ended up in the ER twice. Someone agreeing to that level of payment needs to spend time understanding relative risks — what exactly they are paying for, and at least what they are insuring against with their premiums! These extra expenditures are the proverbial two dollars in the earlier example of the meals.

Let's use the common CPT codes 99213 (follow-up office visit, low complexity) and 99214 (follow-up office visit, moderate complexity) as examples. The code 99213 is reimbursed on an average of $83.08 in my southeast region ($66.46 from Medicare and $16.62 from the patient). A 99214 pays on average $121.45 ($97.16 from Medicare and $24.29 from the patient). In other words, if you or a family member were to visit your physician six days a week for the entire year, you would still save money not being insured and paying the cash price equivalent to a Medicare reimbursement. You could go every day of the week if you were only to pay the Medicaid allowable reimbursement)!

After reading that paragraph and your head finally stops spinning, you might be thinking that is an extreme example, and with all the CPT codes, Medicare, and Medicaid, it's still confusing and you don't want to deal with this level of detail. That's understandable, but it just isn't that complicated once someone involved knows the actual level of an expense versus the real risk. After all, something that incorporates 17.7% of GDP in the United States, if properly managed, can add tremendous amounts of money to your bottom line. The opaqueness of the health insurance industry creates a clientele that is ill-equipped to make the best decisions for them and their companies. In more transparent sectors, that is simply not the case.

Let's use your neighbor's home as an example. Say you live in an average middle-class neighborhood in the Midwest with very similar homes, and you paid $200,000 for yours. If your neighbor offered their comparable house at $25,000 your natural thought would be, "Twenty-five thousand dollars is a bargain." Of course, you might also rightly wonder if there is a problem with it. On the opposite end of the spectrum, if they priced it at one million dollars you would likely say, "Absolutely not, it is not worth that!" You would likely wonder what accounts for the difference. Finally, if I asked if you would pay $185,000 you would probably think a little and then decide that amount was pretty close to what it is worth. You don't have to be a real estate expert to make those simple inferences, even with incomplete information. The relative risk is the same in the health insurance industry, yet the data is even less readily accessible.

Insurance and risk management are no different. Providers have metrics (i.e., comps) to determine their minimum expense, their not-to-exceed price, and their expected spend. It is often difficult for executives to see it this way because of the lack of transparency in the industry. The opaqueness is absolutely by design. The more confused the consumer or executive, the more likely they are to keep doing what they have been doing. Essentially, in the fully insured world, you are allowing an insurance company to give you a twelve-month evergreen contract that moves the goalpost—without providing "comps" — to a new, not-to-exceed price each year. It guarantees that you lose every time. That is why implementing a "Next-Gen" type of plan design has no financial risk for most businesses. It is also why the insurance industry does not want the light shined on that fact because the money is made "in the dark."

One aspect of that "darkness" relates to financial risk. When starting their companies, most entrepreneurs likely understood the risk they were taking. In their minds, they were able to plan out that relative risk, manage what they believed they knew, tried to plan for what they did not know or could not account for, and were still able to put their plan in motion. Your business was probably created as a solution to a need. In that spirit, our solution is the need for you to change the way you look at providing healthcare benefits for your employees and understand this aspect of relative risk. Utilizing programs with Transparent Pharmacy Benefit Managers, Direct Hospital Contracting, Medical Management, Direct Primary Care, and so on, needs to be explored through that same lens. These healthcare expenses in the United States are not just a problem. They are what Warren Buffet referred to as "a tapeworm in the American economy." They are the hidden hazard to your business.

With Next-Gen and similar plans incorporating those previously mentioned programs, you start down a path that decreases your healthcare expenses with no financial downside risk. Plus, the real risk of catastrophic loss simply is not there.

The firm and unequivocal statements about there being no risk of a financial downside or catastrophic loss are true because of something known as stop-loss insurance. When an employer buys a fully insured health insurance plan from one of the major health insurance companies (Blue Cross, United, Cigna, Aetna, Humana, etc.), they purchase an insurance policy. It is not a health insurance policy.

It is a "casualty" insurance policy that reimburses them for claims above a specific number. Usually, that number is somewhere above $175,000, and for a company large enough, that amount might be $500,000. The "health insurance carrier" does it this way to "cede" the risk to another insurance company. That other insurance company doesn't have expertise in administering claims for doctor visits and prescription drugs, but they do have experience pricing premiums at a specific dollar amount across many companies to the point where they feel comfortable with the money they are receiving in premiums. Your fully insured health insurance carrier takes out stop-loss insurance that ensures they do not incur charges from any one person or condition that makes it untenable.

That explains why only a portion of your premium goes towards protection against catastrophic loss. The rest of your premium goes to the previously mentioned intermediaries and paying less expensive claims. Therefore, companies do not need to take such a large risk on every member as a potential "outlier expense." Implementing stop-loss creates the "bookends" to guarantee that you do not lose more than you can afford. After you have secured stop-loss insurance to protect against your worst-case scenarios (those outliers), then you are at liberty to take control of just the average costs of your health plan and eliminate those middlemen.

As mentioned in this chapter and addressed in various ways throughout the book, we are deconstructing the pieces to the puzzle that the prominent carriers of the United States have created by bundling to make things "easy to understand" and "user friendly" for employees. However, this bundling by the large carriers is bankrupting the American worker. Stagnant wages have been mainly due to increased health insurance premiums and an employer's need to pass those costs on to employees.

Finally, being fully insured is not a safer, more protected option. Instead, being fully insured is a decision made by a management team so they don't truly have to manage their healthcare plan. The risk in the fully insured world and the self-insured world is precisely the same. You pay a premium and you have a not-to-exceed amount that prevents you from taking on more liability than you want to accept. The sole difference is this: when you are self-insured, utilizing programs such as transparent Pharmacy Benefit Managers (PBMs), direct hospital contracting, medical management, and direct primary care allows you to be in control of what you want your employee benefits and costs to be. It is simply not the case that health insurance is different from any other business regarding basic business principles such as supply and demand, negotiations, market share, and cost versus quality. Health insurance follows the same business principles, it is just that in this industry the principles are more complex and the price tag is rising due to hidden costs. Please learn the real risk, and remember to always keep that risk relative.

Griffin Meredith

CEO
Commonwealth Insurance Partners

GRIFFIN has been involved in the Risk Management and Healthcare industry since obtaining his bachelor's degree from Centre College. Griffin's company, Commonwealth Insurance Partners (CIP), has a hyper-focus on risk management of health plans. Griffin and his CIP team guide their clients to understanding that surface-level changes without the proper underlying fixes are only temporary solutions to long-term problems.

Griffin has served as President of the Louisville and Kentucky chapters of the National Association of Health Underwriters (NAHU) and received personal certifications from NAHU in Self-Funding, PPACA, Wellness, and Consumer Driven Healthcare. Commonwealth Insurance Partners is the exclusive provider and risk manager for the Kentucky Association of Manufacturers Association Health Plan, which collectively manages the risk for hundreds of employers and thousands of employees.

In addition, Griffin serves as Secretary and Director of Lincoln National Bank, a $380 Million Kentucky-based community bank. He has been recognized as one of "Kentucky's People to Know in Insurance," a Mastermind Partner with the Next-Gen Benefits Healthcare Network, and a Health Rosetta Certified Employee Benefits Advisor. Griffin resides in Louisville, KY, with his wife Sara, who works with the Thoroughbred Retirement Foundation, and his two children Maddox and Margaux.

CONTACT INFO

Connect with Griffin on LinkedIn at: linkedin.com/in/ griffin-meredith-healthcare-advisor-manufacturers-consultant-082a8122

(502)-631-9600 | gmeredith@cipky.com | www.cipky.com
550 S. 5th St., Ste. 101, Louisville, KY 40202

LinkedIn: https://www.linkedin.com/company/commonwealth-insurance-partners
Twitter: https://twitter.com/CIP_KY
Facebook: https://business.facebook.com/commonwealthinsurancepartners/

10

Advisor Advocacy — Building a New Box

by Thomas J. Stautberg

THERE'S NO QUESTION THAT THE benefits industry needs to change. With constant increases in costs — all of which occur without improvement in the quality of care employees receive — both employers and benefits advisers are faced with the question of how to improve the employee benefits experience. Years of the same high-cost, low-quality healthcare have led many brokers to believe that thinking outside the benefits box is the solution, leading to weak loopholes and ineffective quick-fixes that only postpone or marginally dampen the negative effects of the current system. In reality, though, getting rid of the box altogether and building a new one will lead to a far better outcome for your employees and your business as a whole.

The Problem With Your Box

Imagine you're packing up your belongings to move. You find a large box suitable for holding a lot of important items, but it's falling apart. The sides are flimsy and caving in, requiring a lot of duct tape just to keep them up, and every time you lift it, you have to support the bottom with your hand (and more duct tape) to stop its contents from falling straight through. Although the box might have once been useful, it's now so flimsy and broken that the amount of work required to keep it together far outweighs its usefulness.

Would you rearrange your moving process to accommodate that dilapidated box? Or would you simply throw it away and find another solution?

The health insurance box, at this point, is also damaged beyond repair. Yet, many brokers and business owners believe the solution is to think "outside" the box, attempting to tape the system together with HMOs, PPOs, and other short-term fixes. These types of tools and organizations may temporarily seal the cracks within status quo benefits plans, but over time, broker commissions, administration fees, and premiums become heavier, exposing the flaws in the system and eventually rendering it unsustainable.

This chaotic, unmanageable state of the benefits industry can lead to hundreds of thousands of dollars in unnecessary costs for individual businesses every year. Business owners aren't the only ones to bear the weight of it, either — employees also suffer from low-quality care and unnecessary procedures while paying for it with rising deductibles and avoidable copays.

Consider, for example, how the current system can lead to not only higher hospital bills, but also more hospital claims. Many employees don't understand the range or quality of healthcare options available to them, so when a doctor suggests they undergo an operation, they assume that a hospital is their best choice. In reality, though, an outpatient surgery center that specializes in their specific surgical needs is likely to deliver better care at a fraction of the cost of the hospital. For example, data from New Choice

Health shows that the national average cost of arthroscopic shoulder surgery is $25,925, but the average cost for outpatient surgery is just $16,150. Under a status-quo benefits plan that $10,000 would likely be wasted on lower-quality care, and the employee would walk away thinking they'd received the best care at the best price they could hope for.

In fact, there are many surgeries and invasive medical procedures that may not be necessary at all. A report from USA Today revealed that unnecessary operations — of which hysterectomies, spinal surgeries, knee replacements, cesarean sections, and some cardiac procedures are particularly prevalent — may comprise between 10 and 20 percent of all surgeries. Consider how much time, money, and discomfort your employees could be spared if they had the option to be referred to a physiotherapist instead of undergoing knee surgery that they didn't need in the first place.

Prescription costs, too, are often far higher under status-quo benefits plans. Large carriers own pharmacy benefits managers (PBMs) and partner with drug and lab companies, allowing them to make more money from tests and prescriptions that are often excessive in cost or even completely unnecessary. In fact, many large pharmaceutical companies will raise drug prices in response to lower numbers of elective procedures and check-ups. Reuters revealed that in 2020, drugmakers increased the prices of over 860 medications by an average of five percent. Even if none of your employees receive any major procedures in a given year, inflated drug prices can cost them (and your business) thousands in unnecessary expenses.

These factors, among others, can contribute to rising premiums as employees opt for expensive and unnecessary procedures when they don't realize less invasive, cost-saving alternatives might be available. The money they save could be better spent on bills, vacations, or virtually anything else. The constant rise in premiums also adds tens or even hundreds of thousands of dollars in unnecessary expenses for businesses every year. This money could instead be used to expand your business or provide higher employee salaries.

The worst aspect of the status-quo benefits system is that the excessive expenses don't reflect the quality of patient care. A report from the AMA Journal of Ethics revealed a weak and "cloudy" correlation between the cost of healthcare in the United States and the quality of care received by patients. Additionally, rising deductibles often mean that employees have to spend thousands out of pocket before their insurance kicks in. The amount of coverage a company's plan provides is irrelevant if the employees can't afford their $4,000 deductible.

While the current system is a burdensome expense for both employers and employees, it's a boon for status-quo brokers and insurance carriers. There's no incentive for them to improve the current box design when brokers are still getting commissions and carriers continue to profit from astronomical healthcare costs. Your benefits plan should, well, benefit your employees and your business, but unless you're working with a next-generation benefits adviser, your company is likely leaking thousands of dollars through the cracks in your old, broken box.

Building a New Box

Once the old box has been thrown away for good, it's time to build a new one. The process may seem intimidating — especially for business owners who have been immersed in the status-quo benefits system for years — but a next-generation benefits adviser can help.

The first step involves understanding what's important to your business. Both you and your C-suite should discover the answers to these questions: What are our goals and priorities? What needs do our employees have? What are our costs and current challenges?

The answers can help your adviser understand what you're working toward, enabling them to build a benefits plan based on your business' specific needs. A great adviser may have tools to help them access your data, allowing them to see your benefits spending over the lifespan of your company. This, in essence, allows them to see the design of your old box, giving them the information they need to improve upon the materials and construction for the new and improved version.

The changes a great adviser can make to your plan will lead to significant improvements, but as with any major upgrade, you have to be willing to maintain an open mind. There is an adjustment period just like there is when you purchase a new phone, for example. When you switch to the newer model you might find yourself frustrated since the icons and buttons aren't where you are used to finding them. And even though the fancy new technology may be part of what convinced you to buy the phone in the first place, figuring out how to use it can be a long and unpleasant part of the experience.

What stops us from throwing our new devices out the window on day one is the trust we put in the manufacturer to produce a high-quality product. As a business owner, you should put the same trust in your benefits adviser. A great adviser will work with you to determine a rate of change that suits you, your business, and your employees, ensuring that you're not making a sudden transition from a cardboard box to a steel safe with a biometric lock. As the employer, your job is to work with your adviser, keeping an open mind and trusting that the process, while sometimes uncomfortable in the beginning, will ultimately create savings and growth for your business.

You won't be going through the transition alone, either. While "traditional" benefits plans often leave employers and employees in the dark, a great adviser will ensure that you have advocates on your side. Many business owners are accustomed to meeting with their broker just once a year, usually when it's time to renew their plan. However, your adviser should work with you continuously to ensure that the changes being made within your plan reflect the ever-evolving nature of your business. As these changes take place, your adviser will be on your side to help you better understand the way your plan is developing, answer any questions, and adjust your plan as needed.

Your employees, too, will have advocates on their side. Next-generation advisers put employees at the forefront of any good benefits plan, which includes implementing an employee education program so workers can understand their plan. Patient advocacy is another way next-generation benefits plans can work for your employees, giving them access to someone who's an expert in putting patients at ease during hospital stays. Through a next-generation benefits plan, neither you nor your employees have to navigate the benefits system alone.

The key to a truly effective benefits plan is often the medical management firm you choose to work with. This will often be the determining factor for whether your employees will pay too much for lesser quality care, or if they'll save thousands without compromising on care quality. For example, rather than a medical management firm that issues a blanket authorization for an MRI, your adviser can connect you with a firm that sends your employee to a different (less expensive) location twenty minutes away from their home. Rather than incurring a $2,000 cost at the hospital, your employee is only charged $500 for the same procedure. Then, to thank them for traveling a bit farther to get their MRI at a lower cost, your company can cover the bill. In this way, the employee is incentivized to go out of their way to receive the same quality of care at a lower cost, and the business still saves money even if you cover the entire procedure. A great benefits plan often involves teamwork between employer and employee, and together, you can turn a good medical management firm into an effective tool for your business.

This same concept can be applied to other tools in your benefits plan, especially when it comes to prescriptions. Working with a transparent PBM who aims to lower drug costs for your business can cut costs further for you and your staff, and a great adviser will also be able to source your employees' medication. These strategies alone can cut costs by thousands, often without any extra effort or compromise from your employees.

For employers who have been working with a status-quo broker for years, these strategies may seem overly optimistic. In reality, though, a next-generation benefits adviser can and will use the tools at their disposal to build a plan that prioritizes people. Rather than focusing on how to keep your old box from falling apart, they'll dedicate their efforts to building a box that costs less without compromising on quality. The material or shape may be different than what you're used to, but over time, and with support from your adviser, you'll begin to see how a better benefits plan can positively impact your business.

Choosing the Adviser for Your New Box

Once you've decided to throw away your old box, it's time to decide who will help you build a new one. This isn't a decision to be taken lightly. Your benefits plan is likely among your business' top three expenses, and choosing the right person to drive this important change in your company is just as important as finding the right architect for a building project.

As you begin your search for an adviser who will work with and for you and your employees, consider these important factors:

1. Are your incentives aligned?

Misaligned incentives are one of the main reasons business owners overspend on benefits. Brokers generally work for the insurance carrier, earning commission when a client renews their contract. Because their incentives aren't aligned with the business owner's, they have no reason to try to lower the company's spending. A lack of transparency is also a risk; they may get paid more to sell a certain type of plan, which can result in you agreeing to pay even more for a plan that offers you less.

A worthwhile adviser, however, will work on performance-based pay. For example, your agreement with your adviser may say that they get paid a percentage of your total savings. If their initial promises fall flat and you end up saving nothing under their guidance, they don't get paid. If, however, they save you hundreds of thousands of dollars, that's more money for both them and you. They're incentivized to work harder to create savings for you rather than working hard to sell a plan that puts more money in the pockets of the big insurance carriers.

Many brokers have long-standing relationships with the company, and if you generally enjoy their service but still want to improve your benefits plan, you may also want to work with an adviser who acts as a consultant between you and your broker. In these cases, your adviser may charge a consulting fee, a percentage of your savings, or some combination of both. By working with your broker on your behalf, your adviser can provide their expertise to create savings and growth for your business without forcing you to stop working with your broker.

2. Does the adviser have a history of innovation?

Unless you want your new box to look and work the same as the old one, your adviser will need to be innovative. Ask your prospective adviser about what they've done in the past to help businesses rebuild their benefits plans. Are they using the latest tools and strategies to deliver proven results? Have they made big changes to other clients' plans? If so, how much did the clients save as a result? While change can be scary, especially when it comes to a significant expense in your business, an adviser with a record of avoiding change is just a broker with a different job title. Just as a rigid mindset as a business owner can stifle your plan's potential for growth, an adviser who is reluctant to break the mold can limit your savings and waste your time.

3. Do they have experience thinking and working at the C-suite level?

Creating savings isn't automatically enough to turn your benefits plan into a strategic advantage for your business. Unlike a broker who will likely deal primarily with HR when it's time to renew your contract, your adviser will be working closely with your C-suite to ensure that the extra funds obtained through your benefits plan will be used to ensure optimal growth for your company.

Your C-suite knows your business inside and out, and your adviser will need to be on their level to understand the specific needs, goals, and challenges of your business. Your C-suite and your adviser will have a more productive working relationship if they can communicate effectively about what your business needs and how your benefits plan can contribute to those goals. If your adviser doesn't have this experience, it may limit their ability to turn your plan into a savings-generating tool for your company.

4. Do they approach businesses with a flexible mindset?

Every business is different, and a benefits plan that serves one company perfectly may be a terrible fit for yours. If a prospective adviser tells you all about the exciting tools and strategies they want to use for your business' benefits plan before you've even had a conversation about your company goals, this can be a red flag. While an adviser who has these resources at their disposal can be valuable for your company, your business will be better off working with an adviser who knows which tools to include and exclude in their approach. A "one-size-fits-all" benefits plan is rarely a perfect fit.

Your adviser should also be willing to work with your business throughout the year, not just when it's time for your renewal. Your company will evolve over time, and your adviser should take an adaptive approach with your business instead of assuming that what was effective in the beginning of the year will still be effective at the end of the year. Working with an adviser who embraces the unique needs of individual businesses is crucial to unlocking the full potential of your benefits plan.

Just as you'd be selective about the mechanic you entrust with your car, you can (and should) take the same care when deciding which benefits adviser to work with. The wrong one will hand you the same box you've been struggling with for years, but the right one will give you a new and improved design with features that evolve alongside your company, creating savings for years to come.

A Box That Works for You

Rather than fumbling with an outdated benefits plan that no longer suits your company's needs, stop trying to think outside the box. Instead, work with an adviser who knows how to build a better one. The status-quo benefits plan business owners have been trained to accept is flawed beyond repair, draining employers and employees of their hard-earned money without providing a quality of care that reflects the cost. Working with an adviser who keeps your best interests in mind and aligns their incentives with yours allows you to give your employees the care they deserve while utilizing your plan's full potential as a strategic advantage for your business — no duct tape required.

Tom Stautberg

Managing Principal
Stautberg Benefit Advisors

TOM serves c-suite executives who want to break through the status quo by helping them uncover, identify, and eliminate the medical spend "waste" that exists in most health plans. He works with progressive organizations who value their employees and want to offer the best possible employee benefits experience for them. He and his team help these companies build and implement healthcare cost containment strategies to control runaway healthcare costs.

By reducing costs through his firm's Healthcare Cost Containment Solutions, employers create a competitive advantage through talent acquisition and enhanced net profits.

CONTACT INFO ———————————————————————

(513)-620-7200
tom@stautberg.com
www.stautberg.com

.

11

Managing the Cost of Healthcare: A Brief Guide for C-Level Executives

by Ray Kober

I BELIEVE CEOs ARE BORN, not made. As a person who was born into the desire to transform and be a visionary in this world and contribute to it in ways that are not apparent, I must confess that health insurance was not my first chosen profession. Life's path is rarely, if ever, clear and smooth. Having endured the stress and trauma of loved ones battling disease, undergoing surgery, and experiencing financial hardship along with the realization that much of healthcare is a rigged game where the cards are clearly stacked against us stirred a passion in me to act. As CEO of Benefixa, I have the privilege of managing a team dedicated to positive transformation. Together, along with the employers who entrust us with their employees, we have the power to literally save lives, spare people from financial ruin and catalyze the growth of their organizations.

As business leaders, I believe we have an obligation to put people first. Every recommendation we propose begins with a simple question: Will this strategy be better for team members? If it can't pass that test, the strategy does not merit further exploration. The best strategies reduce the cost of healthcare while improving the quality of healthcare for all members.

We all want good health. When our bodies and our minds are healthy, our quality of life is optimal. It seems that it's only when we're suffering with an illness or nursing an injury that we truly appreciate the good health we so often take for granted. Good health is the product of what we eat and drink — you really are what you eat — and what you eat, eats. Eating clean, organic where possible, and non-processed foods is the easy button your body needs to run optimally. Getting proper rest and exercise is also key. It's also about the choices we make when we're in need of medical care. The options we have and the providers we choose could have impactful consequences on our quality of life, and in extreme circumstances, life itself.

Before I jump right into the four steps you can take to transform your healthcare plan, I'd like to share personal experiences that have impacted and shaped my life. My hope is that they lend some perspective. First, it's important to know that while reducing costs is key, we must never lose sight of the prime directive, which is people. Every decision we make with respect to healthcare impacts lives. Before embarking on any journey to change we must first consider our people, their husbands, wives, partners, and children. No one expects to have a cancer diagnosis (or any illness for that matter), befall them or their loved ones. No one expects to be involved in a catastrophic accident, but people face them every day. Our job as leaders is to ensure our people are prepared. When your team members know you not only care about their productivity, but that you have their back when the days are darkest, that's where the magic is. If you've led people for long enough, you know that you don't know what you don't know. Sometimes team members are suffering with healthcare stresses, theirs or family members, and it is reflected in their performance or behavior. Even the best leaders can be out of touch and not know about an underlying health issue at the root of this problem. Having the right healthcare plan will put your team in the best position to manage a catastrophic health event and transform you into a Hero leader!

I've had multiple encounters with the healthcare system. Now that I think about it, healthcare has affected my entire life beginning with my dad's diagnosis of lung cancer in 1967. I was a baby, but his diagnosis set our family into a tailspin. There were many doctor visits, including a trip to Dallas, Texas in search of a cure. He succumbed to the illness shortly after my second birthday in 1968.

Fast forward to 1992. My wife Maria, pregnant with our first child, went in for a routine ultrasound. The technician had her on the table for an unusually long period of time which understandably gave her anxiety. We later learn from her OBGYN that they found what they assumed to be a little extra piece of lung tissue lodged beneath his diaphragm. The medical term is a sub diaphragmatic pulmonic sequestration. It was recommended that he have surgery to remove the tissue and confirm their assumption. We met with pediatric surgeons at Columbia and NYU and ultimately settled on Howard Ginsberg, M.D. at NYU. Let me tell you, I have never felt so helpless and vulnerable as when they wheeled our infant son through the operating room doors to take him in for surgery. Thank God he went through surgery without a hitch and Dr. Ginsberg confirmed that indeed, it was lung tissue.

Four years later and now a kindergartener, Ray was having severe stomach pain and began vomiting. Normally, after throwing up, you feel better and sleep it off, but his pain was increasing in severity, and he continued to vomit. He also wasn't passing gas and hadn't had a bowel movement in some time. It turns out that he had a bowel adhesion. Anytime you have abdominal surgery there's a risk that scar tissue can ensnare and strangle your intestine. Emergency surgery is indicated because if the blood supply to the intestines is cut off for too long it can lead to other significant medical complications. We took him to the ER at North Shore on Long Island, met with Dr. Lee who confirmed that he needed emergency surgery, and my wife and I got to see young Raymond rolled through the O.R. doors a second time. It's hard to believe, but the second time was even more emotionally devastating than the first! I am happy to report that other than a few bumps and breaks (yes, the boy wonder broke his fibula playing club rugby at BU), today he's doing well as an accomplished mechanical engineer and MBA.

Not to be outdone, my daughter Alexa gave us a scare recently when she began having heart palpitations. She said her heart would just start racing for no reason at all. We had her see a cardiac specialist who outfitted her with a heart monitor that she was to wear for four or five days. We never made it that far. The first day she wore the device I called to check in and see how she was doing and she said, "Not good!" "What's going on?" I asked. "Well, I just walked to Key Food (ten-minute walk) to get a few things, got to the check-out line and felt like my heart was beating out of my chest!" That led us to the ER at St. Francis Hospital on Long Island where they did not observe a rapid heartbeat, but based on her symptoms, recommended an EP (electro physiology) study. The next day, our twenty-two-year-old baby was subjected to an invasive exam where, while awake on the table, the doctor threaded wires through arteries in her groin and neck to observe the heart function as adrenaline was injected to produce a rapid heartbeat. Her surgeon's observation confirmed a circular pattern of blood flow indicative of what in laymen's terms I would describe as a short-circuit. The surgeon ablated the anomalous tissue and within an hour the procedure was done. I'm thrilled to report that Alexa is doing well today!

In the case of my son's first surgery, my wife and I were in our mid-twenties, not experienced in these matters, and selected the best of the surgeons referred to us by her OBGYN. We did our research, interviewed two surgeons, and made the best decision we could. His second surgery and my daughter's procedure were done on an emergency basis so we did not have the luxury of time. We did not have a medical concierge to guide our decision, and if you think about it, most of us are not the best decision makers when there's a loaded gun pointed at our heads. Our decisions were based on having faith in the hospitals, on their word-of-mouth reputation, and a shotgun review of the surgeons. Knowing what I do now, a much better approach is to have access to a medical professional who will guide these decisions. The basis for their guidance is rooted in their medical expertise and access to the providers data (scorecards). I think you'll agree it's a much better approach than throwing a dart, randomly picking an in-network provider, basing your decision on hearsay, or relying on your judgement while under duress.

When a medical crisis hits you want to know you have access to the best medical care possible. What does that even mean? What is the best medical care possible? No one wants to be told where they can and can't go for medical care. Yet most of us are not capable of discerning good, from bad, from mediocre. How should an employer go about the business of safeguarding their employees? The culture of your organization is the heartbeat of your organization. While you should spare no expense to protect and nurture your employees, the fact of the matter is that the highest quality healthcare is often the least costly. Following are my suggestions for getting a handle on this huge SG&A expense. More important than money, is taking a people-first approach and living up to your fiduciary responsibility to make all decisions with their benefit and welfare in mind. The funny thing is, when you put people first, culture soars, recruiting goes up, retention increases, turnover decreases, and money flows to the bottom line.

The quest for higher quality, lower cost care is a process. It's a journey that can be distilled into four pillars, each of which provides value to you as a CEO because you're going to gain insight. It provides value to your executive team by bringing them closer to their goals of reducing costs and increasing the bottom line, and it brings value to your employees because your team is invested in them. They will appreciate that fact. Nailing each of the following four pillars will get you where you want to go.

I — Know Your Numbers

What's your goal? If you don't have a goal, you'll never reach it. The national average spend in 2021 for healthcare according to Kaiser Family Foundation ranges from just approximately $7,700 for individuals to just over $22K for family coverage.

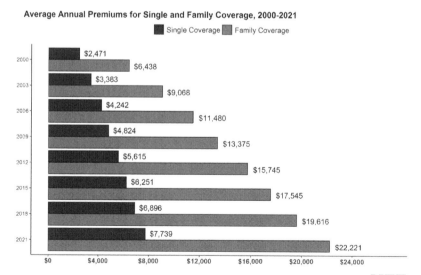

Average Annual Premiums for Single and Family Coverage, 2000-2021

SOURCE: KFF Employer Health Benefits Survey, 2018-2021; Kaiser/HRET Survey of Employer-Sponsored Health Benefits, 2000-2017

This includes worker and employer premium contributions. A NextGen advisor (an advisor whose interests are aligned with your interests) will help you analyze your workforce and target a per employee per year spend goal. What's your PEPY goal? If you don't have a handle on this, then your number one SG&A expense after payroll might as well be a runaway train. You must get a handle on this number. It would stand to reason that if you manage a team of young folks who rarely utilize healthcare, your target should be lower than that of a workforce twice their age managing chronic illnesses. We are biological and mechanical. Over time, stuff breaks down. The risk for medical care goes up and so does the cost for insurance. There are also increased risks to account for with a young population such as premature babies that may spend time in the NICU, fertility treatment, etc. Your NextGen advisor will work with your team and actuaries to zero in on the appropriate risk to plan for your specific group. This is a math exercise. They will help you arrive at an appropriate PEPY target and set a goal.

Fifteen to twenty percent of your healthcare spend is administration. There is not much opportunity for savings here which brings us to where the money is, claims. Claims constitute 80 percent of your spend. Actuarially, here is how the numbers break down: 20 percent of your members consume 80 percent of your claims; 5 percent consume 50-60 percent and one percent accounts for approximately 25 percent of your claims.

Graphically it looks like this:

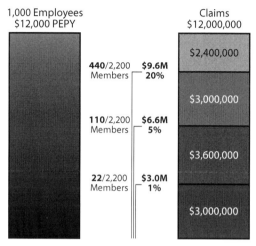

KNOW YOUR NUMBERS
20% OF YOUR MEMBERS CONSUME 80% OF CLAIMS

1,000 Employees
$12,000 PEPY

Claims
$12,000,000

$2,400,000

440/2,200 Members — $9.6M 20%

$3,000,000

110/2,200 Members — $6.6M 5%

$3,600,000

22/2,200 Members — $3.0M 1%

$3,000,000

CURRENT AVERAGE MEMBER CLAIM PMPY

SUPER UTILIZER POPULATION
22 @ $136,364 = $3,000,000
88 @ $40,909 = $3,600,000

MEMBER CLAIMS
20% = 440 @ $21,818 = $9,600,000
80% = 1,760 @ $1,364 = $2,400,000

PEPY = PER EMPLOYEE PER YEAR • PMPY = PER MEMBER PER YEAR • 2,200 PLAN MEMBERS

In this example your PEPY is $12K, and below the national average of approximately $15K. If this is your organization, you might be feeling pretty good about yourself. And if you use the national average as a benchmark, you'd be right to feel good about yourself unless you learned that you were paying as much as 3X too much and, most importantly, had your team exposed to misdiagnosis, infections, botched surgeries requiring readmissions, predatory medical practices, predatory billing practices, financial hardship, stress, bankruptcy, and death! If that sounds far-fetched, guess again. It's reality.

Key Takeaways: CEOs and executive teams now understand that controlling claims, particularly high claimants, is key to lowering costs. The better they can manage those members, the better they can control costs. Employees will benefit from a better managed plan and suffer less severe increases.

II — Strive for Total Transparency

Any good CFO can rattle off a list of their largest expenses and break them down in granular detail. Optimizing supply chain management in all aspects of procurement is key to organizational success. Yet when it comes to the #1 SG&A expense after payroll, healthcare, you can't tell me the cost of anything! That's a problem and it's not an accident. Most of my work is conducted in the large and enterprise employer space where leadership has figured out that you simply can't know the cost of anything in a fully insured plan, and therefore are at least partially self-insured. It's really a backwards process where we are at the mercy of the system. What I mean by that is simple. What's the cost for a trip to the doctor? How about a specialist, an MRI, a CT scan with or without contrast, or an ultrasound? What's the cost for knee or hip surgery; total or partial? What's the cost for any one of thousands of prescription drugs? You don't know the answer to any of these questions. None of us do because we don't know how to know. We don't shop for medical care, or if we do, we do it badly. We don't know how to shop for quality, and we certainly don't know the cost of anything. We figure that out on the back end after services have been rendered. If your health plan is like most health plans and you're being honest, you know this is true.

The good news is that a NextGen health plan delivers transparency, and with transparency comes control. Quality, predictability, and control. The path to transparency begins with aligning yourself with partners who are committed to delivering transparency. This means breaking away from the status quo. It's a departure, a bon voyage, an arrivederci to the bloated world of the fully insured. We must realize that picking from an assortment of poor plans will leave us with a poor plan. ***We must strive for transparency in health-care and that means managing healthcare prospectively before we incur a charge.*** If our employees are only focused on their copay or their co-insurance then our plan will never break free from the powerful vortex, the allure, the myth of taking comfort in having that BUCAH [Blue Cross, United, Cigna, Aetna (CVS), Humana] logo on your insurance ID card.

Key Takeaways: CEOs and executive teams must insist on healthcare transparency. With transparency comes the ability to manage the supply chain along with budget certainty. Employees benefit from a plan that is no longer price gouging them on the front end at point of service, or the back end with increases that are not justified.

III — HIGH COST ≠ HIGH QUALITY

Transparency in healthcare means having tools to assess and score the quality of providers and compare costs. Today, many people are under the false impression that if they have United or Aetna or Cigna on their ID card and their out-of-pocket exposure is low, they have great healthcare. I am sorry to say that it probably means you are paying too much for insurance and that in actuality your healthcare is no better or worse than anyone else's. You see, health insurance is not healthcare. Recently, someone close to me was diagnosed with a glioblastoma, aka brain cancer. The diagnosis is horrible and, in short, due to the nature of the disease it is treatable, but not curable. He had what most would consider good insurance, multiple policies in fact, with large publicly traded insurance carriers providing access to a broad network of providers. He had surgery at Columbia in Manhattan by a surgeon who went to an ivy league medical school and has numerous accolades and accreditations. However, I found out later that his quality score is an abysmal 12.7 out of a total possible 100! The metrics for the score include mortality, complications, readmissions, patient safety and inpatient quality. He rated excellent in mortality and patient safety, but poor in complications and very poor in readmissions. We did find another surgeon in the same practice with a quality score of 99.5. To be clear, these numbers do not ensure a favorable health outcome, but if you had access to the data and were in the process of selecting a surgeon for a life-or-death procedure, which one would you choose? We must trust math and science. With the right partners, your team members will be armed with an informed medical opinion, have access to the best data, and be led to the highest quality providers at the best price.

It's counterintuitive, but in healthcare, the lowest cost typically correlates to the highest quality.

Key Takeaways: CEOs and executive teams now understand that simply giving team members access to broad provider networks does not ensure quality. Furthermore, poor provider choices lead to higher risk and increased costs. Employees will benefit from better outcomes at lower costs.

IV — Think Big — Really Move the Needle

Referring to the numbers above in I, 20 percent of your members drive 80 percent of your claims, and claims make up 80 percent of your health insurance expense. It stands to reason that if there was a way to shrink the pool of high claimants, the spend would go down and your PEPY would be heading in the right direction. Simple math: 1,000 members spending 10K (claims) PEPY = $10M total claims spend. If I could remove 100 members spending an average of $50K each in claims PEPY, I'd now be spending $5M or $5,555 PEPY ($5M/900). If only it was that easy. What if I told you it isn't as hard as you might think?

Most working-class people have far less than $1,000 saved for a rainy day. This has been well documented for decades (see Elizabeth Warren's article in the Washington Post, 2005 — Sick & Broke, https://www.washingtonpost.com/archive/opinions/2005/02/09/sick-and-broke/1213a14f-e083-4dad-87eb-b6290447de98/) and while it may seem counterintuitive, this statistic applies to six-figure, dual-income households. ***Folks are living paycheck to paycheck. They can't afford the out-of-pocket costs associated with high deductible plans. If you could add a voluntary employee benefit to your offering that relieved them of this burden and simultaneously printed money to your bottom line, would you?***

One of Benefixa's cornerstone strategies to help businesses really move the needle, help employees who are most in need, increase recruiting, retention, and abate future healthcare increases for all is a financial hedging strategy. We've learned that to reduce the cost of healthcare we must reduce the consumption of healthcare. To reduce the risk, we advise taking a team approach by offering employees a new voluntary employee benefit. Give team members a choice to enroll in a plan that will provide 100 percent insurance coverage to them and their family members and simultaneously print money for the organization's bottom line. If that sounds crazy or farfetched, or too good to be true, I can assure you it's not. You picked up this book and have read this far because you'd like to do a better job of managing your healthcare expenses. Think big and be open to new concepts. What you might find after conducting due diligence is that there really are some things that can significantly move the needle that you've never heard of before. The 100 Percent Plan is one of those things.

It would take many more words to communicate this offering thoroughly and completely, but suffice it to say that we have identified a way to hedge financial risk, print money for the bottom line, and most importantly deliver the goods for team members. It's the best insurance coverage anyone can hope for — 100 percent coverage. And while only a segment of your team members will qualify, it typically attracts those who are most in need. Consequently, it serves to de-risk your plan for the benefit of all team members.

Key Takeaways: CEOs and executive teams focused on reducing risk by reducing the number of super-utilizers will be well on their way to lowering costs, reducing risk, and controlling future costs. Employees with access to 100 percent coverage have the best insurance coverage imaginable.

I founded Benefixa because I am passionate about helping working-class people appreciate a better quality of life. I come from a working-class background and have first-hand experience navigating our healthcare system. The healthcare you provide your employees is more than a line item on a budget sheet. You can choose to gloss over it, budget for increases, and remain status quo with the thought that if you're spending top dollar that you're providing the best care possible. Or, based upon what you now know, you can champion a plan that delivers life-changing results and simultaneously delivers on all fronts for all stakeholders. It's not uncommon for our team to save plans 30-60 percent while significantly improving benefits for everyone.

Ray Kober

CEO, Benefixa

RAY KOBER is a dynamic entrepreneur with twenty years of experience in insurance. He started his insurance career at Aflac in 2001, was named Rookie of the Year in New York Metro, and went on to lead Aflac's Region in New York's Westchester County.

Ray has vast experience in the employee benefits space having lead initiatives on hundreds of projects and managed teams serving hundreds of thousands of employees.

As CEO of Benefixa, Ray is committed to helping businesses reverse the trend of insurance increases that have plagued society. He leads a team that works tirelessly to advocate for working class people, the men and women who are the fabric and heartbeat of America. "Ultimately, healthcare is about human lives. And when you think about it, people are what really matter. When you start there, you are on the path to fixing healthcare in the United States of America."

Ray has been a member of the largest network of c-level executives, The C-Suite Network, since 2018 and is an advisory board member of The HERO Club exclusively reserved for founders and CEOs. He's an avid investor, a strong proponent of green energy, EVs, cryptocurrency, biomedicine, blockchain technology and America 2.0.

CONTACT INFO ———————————————————————

1-866-800-3433

ray@benefixa.com

www.benefixa.com

Learn, grow and take action here: benefixa.com/bonus

12

Successfully Managing the Healthcare Supply Chain

by Ryan Spencer

N A PAST LIFE, I worked at an engine company. While here, one of my responsibilities was overseeing engine quality as they were installed into a variety of different truck configurations to be sold. Beginning one week, as I was working through my email inbox an email arrived with the subject, 'pinched oil line'. I carefully scrolled through the pictures. In one, a red circle highlighted a flexible tube (the oil line) being bent at an unusual angle pushed in by a metal air pipe that supplied air to the engine. This was a huge problem. I quickly went back to the designs and designers, trying to understand what happened and ensure this was not standard or a design flaw. In my role, one case was an anomaly, a few cases was considered a trend, more than that constituted a problem, and this particular problem was picking up steam quickly.

We moved through the typical checklist: the designs checked out, the issue occurred only on a portion of the engines, and it was found on some trucks that had never been driven or serviced. We headed to the assembly line. As the trucks moved down the line, we watched the wheels and fuel tanks bolted onto the bare metal frame and the wiring get connected. Eventually an engine was lowered in. Watching the engine dropping into place, the problem became clear. The spacing was very tight. To provide a little extra room, a technician took a rubber hammer and hit the metal tube inward, pushing it against the oil line so the engine could be lowered in. After the engine was inside, in most cases the technicians then pulled the part back out, leaving the correct spacing. However, in some cases, they moved too quickly to the next step, leaving the oil line pinched. This one small unmanaged part of the supply chain led to complications, recalls, redesigns, and added cost. Furthermore, in this deviation from a standard process, there was no communication back through to highlight the challenges they were having, leaving them on their own to establish a modification. To work flawlessly, the whole process requires hundreds of suppliers and part markers to work in harmony with the designers, factories, technicians, and field support. If even one small part or player fails, it can bring the entire system to its knees.

I occasionally joke that I traded out my past life in solving engineering problems for a new arena with even more problems to solve. While said in jest, the truth of it is at its core, the healthcare industry is not entirely unlike the supply chain of an engine company. Many constituents need to operate in harmony for the services to happen and people to get care, for the appropriate billing to work between facilities and physicians, and the information to flow so patients can maintain their conditions. While the basic supply chain structures are parallel, the level of oversight and ability to drive quality outcomes and competition are many times far from the same. This chapter outlines five critical areas in the healthcare supply chain that can be 'pinch points' and lead to runaway costs within your plan.

1. Strategic Partnerships

The first point of focus is within what I label Strategic Partnerships. These are the partners that many times are glossed over and grouped under a category deemed administrative costs. Broken out and specifically chosen, they can be your biggest assets. They include your medical carrier, pharmacy benefit manager, broker, medical manager, cost and quality vendor and others. These partnerships can even extend into what I view as the actual "insurance" part of healthcare in a stop loss partner or captive environment. While all these costs combined generally total only 10-20% of your costs, they are absolutely critical in setting a health plan up for success. If you are passive in this selection, you will be signing up for cost increases and broadly following the medical trend increases that are plaguing the country.

To achieve different results, we need to get outside of the inherent misaligned incentives commonly embedded in traditional solutions. The misaligned incentives occur when the partners, either actively selected or bundled within your carrier, make more money when your costs go up and less money if your costs decrease. When these "controllers" or "business managers" you hired to manage your healthcare spend have this arrangement, it creates a push-pull foundation within your plan, making it very difficult to achieve different results. With this in mind, the first step in moving toward control is selecting strategic partners and compensating them in a clear and transparent way. The first and most basic move and check within this topic is moving toward a fee for service-based model instead of compensation through spreads or percentages of premium.

2. Physician Services

With the strategic partner foundation in place, you can turn your focus to the claims. One of the main benefits in selecting the right partners is that you have the flexibility to impact claims. The first area within claims that we focus on is physician services. Physicians are the gatekeepers to the healthcare system, specifically on the primary care and specialist side. Hospitals understand this clearly and have made great strides in adding independent physicians to their staff and targeting the revenue these physicians will bring in on large claims upstream. Within this category, three items are critical to manage care:

- **Low barriers to entry**: People need to be able to see the doctor. The best way to lower catastrophic claims is to manage them on the front end. To do this, people need to be aware of their conditions and follow up on them. If your physician prices are cost prohibitive, causing people to avoid and put off going to the doctor, it will lead to higher and less predictable costs. A lower cost or a telemedicine supplement can help provide access and set the stage for the system to work appropriately.

- **Quality:** The quality of the doctor is a critical piece to the puzzle. Doctors are the "technicians" within this healthcare chain. Much like the experience with the oil line, physicians can have a drastic impact on the outcome and livelihood of the patients. Whether it be unnecessary procedures, deviating from the standard methods, or a track record of complications, creating an environment where your employees have this valuable information is extremely important.

- **Handoffs:** Even if the members begin by selecting a quality physician, the job is not done. Many times, the physician ordering the service is not the one actually performing the procedure. It's important to manage the handoffs in these instances because the system is set up to refer upstream within the given health system, not to focus on the doctors with the highest quality care.

These items are very important in the system, but in most cases, employers are not set up to manage at this level of detail. This is the reason building a strong strategic partner foundation is so critical; they can have the skills and bandwidth to lean in and implement these solutions.

3. Outpatient Procedures

This section is the first one upstream of the physicians. It can be difficult to manage because it is generally a higher volume of procedures, but it can also be one of the most valuable. The costs of these outpatient procedures can vary wildly. I have seen billed charges of $90k for a knee procedure at one facility and $30k at another situated just down the road. The ironic part is that in viewing the quality data, the $30k facility offered a significantly higher quality. This type of scenario is not uncommon. In medical services, there is not a correlation between cost and quality.

Outside of some of the more noninvasive procedures, you also have members with ongoing care under this umbrella. Managing a condition or receiving monthly infusions can have a huge impact on a health plan. Engaging with these members and ensuring quality and efficient care can lead to better outcomes and more present employees.

We have a number of strategies to put guard rails on this segment of claims. Here are two of the top ones to consider.

- **Selecting an aligned Medical Manager:** Each of these segments is tied in some way or another in the healthcare supply chain. Having an aligned medical manager can help create a system of checks and balances between segments.

In this instance, the medical manager can be the backstop for when a physician does not follow guidelines exactly or schedules an unnecessary procedure. This can avoid drastic consequences both to a member's health, and through the cost of paying for unnecessary or incorrect treatment.

- **Bundled Services:** In my opinion, few things are as painful as paying for errors and mistakes. As part of my responsibilities, I oversee our stop loss captives. In doing so, I am acutely aware of the high claims that happen inside the member groups. One scenario popped up when a member went in for a simple outpatient procedure which the physician botched. From there, several follow up procedures were necessary to attempt to correct the initial error. Each of these was at the expense of the employer, not the doctor or hospital that made the mistake. The beauty of bundled services is that it is a bundled and known charge, and it transfers the risk of complications to the facility.

- **Centers of Excellence:** (See the further description within Inpatient section below)

4. Inpatient Procedures

Inpatient procedures are the fewer, high dollar, high risk procedures and care. This is the segment furthest downstream for a patient. The best way to engage and impact these claims is to adequately manage the other areas. Select quality physicians, lower the barriers to care, and manage the handoffs on the front end and it will flow down and create efficiencies within the inpatient arena.

In addition to being intentional with the initial care, many of the larger companies that have been strategic with their healthcare planning and investment are leveraging **Centers of Excellence**, sometimes even sending members across the country to get care because the cost and quality of these procedures is that critical. These Centers of Excellence functionally operate much like the bundled services above, transferring the risk of complications, but integrate a strong quality component into it as well. These offerings can be a great addition and, implemented correctly, can help infuse quality procedures as a staple within your offering.

5. Pharmacy

This section has recently become one of the most visible areas. Legislation around rebates and costs, in combination with the rising costs of specialty medications have pushed the pharmacy to the forefront of conversations. The bright side within this conversation is that it can also be one of the easiest and most impactful areas to manage within your health plan. The reason behind this is that high-cost pharmaceuticals are usually only needed by a very small number of members, typically less than three percent. In addition, there are not the emotional complications of a doctor/patient relationship to factor in. To manage a condition, medications are often ongoing, so the maintenance and costs will continue from year to year. With this in mind, driving efficiencies and reductions in this area can pay enormous dividends for years to come.

The most critical questions to consider when it comes to pharmacy claims and cost are:

- Is your pharmacy benefit manager transparent?
- Is your pharmacy benefit manager flexible?
- Is your pharmacy benefit manager high touch?

Clearly, these questions point to the willingness and aptitude of the pharmacy benefit manager. This is very important. In the past, I had a client spending $90k / year on a medication that I should have been able to source for free, but they did not have the ability to implement the strategy. The following year we switched pharmacy benefit managers and implemented the change immediately, creating a huge benefit for the client AND the patient.

If the program answers yes to all three questions above, they should be realizing all of the rebates, be removed from the spread pricing problems, and be immediately informed of any potential costs or medications coming in that they need to proactively work through.

Conclusion

These five areas are hugely important within a health program. It is paramount to establish critical vendor partners to rearrange and refine the healthcare supply chain to achieve different results. Because of our healthcare system's nature and build, it becomes incumbent upon us to manage the healthcare supply chain and help to identify quality care, control costs, and ensure no one is "banging on the parts in the middle of the system with a rubber hammer". With so many misaligned incentives so often found inside the systems, it is critical to know the watch outs and ensure the partners you pick are knowledgeable and pulling in the same direction as you.

Another critical item to consider is that this is a journey. You likely do not need to drive all of this change at once. That is where having the data is so important. It will show you where to focus. I have a client with a negative renewal trend over the past five years and the only strategies they've implemented are within the pharmacy. We are prepared to roll out those on the inpatient and outpatient procedures and will when the data shows it is necessary and their population is ready to hear it.

Lastly, to fully refine this supply chain, you need constant and clear communication. This communication is between the company and their strategic partners as well as between the company and their members. To ensure proper implementation, the constituents need to know how the process should feel, so when they encounter a process that is slightly different than what they had at their last job or within a poorly managed supply chain, they understand the process is working as intended. With proper and ongoing communication, buy in, and occasionally even incentives for your team and employees to engage, you will see drastically different and better results.

Ryan Spencer

Partner
Conner Insurance

RYAN is an advisor and partner at Conner Insurance, a co-founder of City on a Hill Health, and director of the medical stop loss captives within the organizations. He has found a passion in helping business and schools create efficiencies within their operations and providing enhanced care, additional benefits, and engagement for their workforces.

Before entering the healthcare business, Ryan worked as an engineer for an engine company spanning several roles, including powertrain optimization, combustion performance, and customer relationships and quality. The curiosity and analytical skills he developed during his time as an engineer has aided in his pursuit of better and more efficient care inside of our healthcare system.

His educational background consists of a Bachelor's of Science in Engineering Physics from Taylor University, and a MBA in Marketing and Finance from IU Kelley School of Business. Outside of work, Ryan lives in Carmel, IN and enjoys spending time with his wife and two kids. His hobbies include reading, hiking, and playing cards with friends.

CONTACT INFO —————————————————————

(317)-808-7717
rspencer@connerins.com
www.connerins.com

13

Bacon, Eggs, and Performance-Based Fees — ERISA-Compliant Broker Compensation: Why and Why Now

by Michael Smith

G UY WALKS INTO A LOCAL diner with the key man at Merck. He had just won a lucrative consulting assignment, beating out the big box firms. As they are served their breakfast he asks his new client, "What made you pick my little boutique firm? Those guys had stacks of references and three-inch thick capabilities binders. Heck, they even have commercials during the Superbowl."

The new client said, "You won because they get paid for activity and you get paid for results. It's like my bacon and eggs here. The chicken is involved,…but the pig is committed".

The old yarn about chickens and pigs has been shared by coaches, teachers, drill sergeants, and parents for years. Here, it's the story of Alan Weiss, the innovator of performance-based fee consulting. It is the revenue model that won him the business that day at Merck, and on other days at General Electric, Hewlett-Packard, Mercedes-Benz, Times Mirror, the Federal Reserve, and Toyota.[1]

Throughout the chapters of this book penned by my NextGen colleagues, our national wolfpack of cost containment advisors, we have shown owners, CFOs, …and select HR executives in the "get-it line", lots and lots of reasons to upgrade their healthcare buying process.

Some change. Most don't.

Those who don't sort of understand why they should. However, without compelling answers to their requisite "why now" and "why you" questions, it's business as usual. But those answers are about to get far harder to dismiss with the usual objections of "we like our guy" and "HR doesn't like change".

And that is the subject of this chapter.

Specifically, a COVID-accelerated focus on cutting costs and new ERISA fiduciary rules will combine to check off a whole lot of "why change now" boxes. When they do, like stockbrokers who became fiduciary wealth managers a decade ago, the way benefit brokers are paid will change for the better.

That's because in order to check off the "why me" box, health insurance brokers will need to move to their *clients'* side of the table as their fiduciary, switch to a performance-based fees revenue model, and get committed.

…Like the pig.

The Case for a Trusted Advisor on Your Side of the Table

I began my career in benefits at age 16 at the headquarters of Northrop Corporation. As I proctored secretarial typing tests, my father ran Northrop HR and was their head labor lawyer. He was

1 Weiss, Alan (1992). *Million Dollar Consulting: The Professional Guide to Growing a Practice.* McGraw-Hill.

tapped by Presidents Reagan and Ford to be Deputy Secretary of Labor. Big fish, my dad. Some years after he retired, he shared his disdain for the complexity and cost of providing employer-sponsored healthcare. He described it as being akin to the ladies' menus at fancy restaurants. In the old days, Mom got the full menu, but without prices.

That's how fees work in the American healthcare system. Benefit plan decision makers sit on one side of the table. Alone. With a ladies' menu.

On the other side of the table is the healthcare supply chain:

- **Brokers**…who get a percentage of the ever-increasing premium that is charged by,

- **Insurance companies**…that hide/obscure the cost of claims delivered by,

- **Hospital facilities**…that have 100 different prices for the same procedure and prescribe an ocean of pills from,

- **Pharmacy benefit managers**…that have 32 ways to hide fees from,

- **Administrators**…that pay bills below $15k without even *looking* at them.

OK, remember those big box consultants who bid on that Merck contract? You can't afford to pay their rates, but the companies in the healthcare supply chain sure can. And they do. As an example, one big box consulting firm told a Texas hospital system considering a value-based payment model to "milk" fee-for-service payment as much as they could for as long as they could.[2]

Another accomplice to the crime is McKinsey and Company, the world's most respected consultancy. The distribution of Oxycontin (…bad stuff) escalated when McKinsey (…the world's

---

2   Dr. Eric Bricker (2020). *Consultants Advise on How to Increase Healthcare Costs.* AHealthcareZ.

most respected consultant) advised their client (…now bankrupt) that paying off victims (…who died) would keep the money party going.[3]

So, here is the question. If, on the other side of the table, the medical industrial complex has consultants (…with a body count) to *maximize* their revenue, isn't it time employers have consultants on their side to *minimize* it?

Why Now #1: The 10x View from Ballona Creek

I rowed on the UCLA crew team with a fellow named Scott Galloway. While not as famous as my freshman roommate, NBA legend Reggie Miller, Scott has distinguished himself as a global thought leader. He speaks these days of the post-COVID economy's Great Dispersion: the accelerated shift away from traditional distribution in vulnerable industries.[4]

As of this writing, we are dusting off from a global pandemic that has created, as I paraphrase Scott, a generational opportunity to deliver a product or service with a 10x (meaning ten times) improvement on cost or speed relative to legacy processes. The biggest losers will be sectors that consumers hate the most. For example, the pandemic accelerated the slow deaths of stinky gyms and long commutes by 10x as Peloton and Zoom took over.

As a gauge of the sectors consumers hate the most — and are thereby ready for a 10x acceleration in their demise, look to the Net Promoter Score Index ("NPS"). This ranks customers' overall satisfaction (and dissatisfaction) with a product or service, for example:

---

3 New York Times (11/27 2020). *McKinsey Proposed Paying Pharmacy Companies Rebates for OxyContin Overdoses*
4 Galloway, Scott (2020). *Post Corona: From Crisis to Opportunity.* New York: Portfolio/Penguin.

- Their low NPS Score showed that people hated phone companies, so Motorola found a way to call a person and not a building.
- Cable TV was at the bottom of the NPS Index, so Netflix provided the ability to cut the cord.
- As the hassle of shopping tanked their NPS Index, Amazon pulled stores from the mall to your desktop, to your mobile phone, and to your front door.

As we entered the global pandemic in 2020, care to guess what vertical American's hated about the most? You don't need a consultant to tell you. It's healthcare. And here's the penalty of such a low NPS score according the guy who rowed on Ballona Creek for UCLA in the starboard six seat:

> "One of the greatest transfers in stakeholder value in history is going to happen over the next five years in healthcare, shifting from incumbents to new players."

To give an example, for years, telemedicine had been methodically trying to reshape the distribution of doctor visits by removing unnecessary friction and cost. But before the pandemic, its share of medical consultations was stuck at about one percent. In the eight weeks of the pandemic's first wave, the use of telemedicine rose from one percent of total consultations to 14 percent. Basically, a decade's growth…in *eight weeks*.

What does all this mean for the CEO and CFO managing a healthcare spend in a post-COVID world? It means that their patience with the traditional Kabuki dance of health insurance purchasing is about over. "Costs only go up. A 15 percent hike isn't bad, most are 18 percent. Don't shoot the messenger." …Lather, rinse, repeat.

So why listen to the wolfpack and change from a retail to institutional healthcare design now? Because, for one reason, buyers are ready for 10x dispersions to the healthcare supply chain. Now let's look at the second reason.

Why Now #2: Broker Fiduciary Fee Disclosures

Talk about unlikely bedfellows: On the morning of Dec 27, 2021 and there forward, a Trump administration statue kicks-in that will extend an Obama administration regulation. This will require all group health plan brokers, advisors, and consultants to disclose both direct *and indirect* compensation to their clients under ERISA §408(b)(2).

When I tell you that the new conflict and fee disclosure rules will accelerate the demise of the current "chicken is involved" health insurance brokerage model, I have some credibility — because I'm still bloody from the last battle.

You see, I'm a recovering 401(k) fiduciary strategist. I have testified on Wall Street conflicts of interest before the Securities and Exchange Commission, US Department of Labor, and a committee of the United States Senate. When those same §408(b)(2) fee and conflict disclosures hit 401(k) in 2012, I developed a fee evaluation business. Before then, my partners and I showed Wall Street firms how to give advice on their own variable fee funds. This is a massively profitable, so massively prohibited, transaction. It could only be affected through the licensing of our business method patents as sanctioned by U.S. Department of Labor. Our clients included JPMorgan, AIG/SunAmerica, Wells Fargo, TCW, Voya, and others.[5]

---

5   Federal Register 11/04/1997, Grant of Individual Exemptions; TCW Group and SunAmerica Department of Labor Advisory Opinion 2001-09A.

OK, grab a cup of coffee, here's some legal background. ERISA Section 406 (29 U.S.C. §1106) generally prohibits a fiduciary from providing, directly or indirectly, goods or services between a plan and a "party in interest". The get out of jail card that allows an employer to send plan trust money to a party with said conflict is the ERISA §408(b)(2) exemption. To get it, the plan sponsor now has to:

1. Receive in good order a disclosure of the vendor's services, fees, and conflicts,

2. Find and document that the services provided are necessary, and

3. Opine and document that the fees are reasonable.

Failure to do those three things throws the plan into breach of ERISA. That's a big deal because the plan sponsors then lose protections against *personal* liability.[6]

Let me say that again, failure to document that the broker's fees are reasonable and services necessary exposes the C-Suite to lawsuits by employees who (see above) <u>hate</u> the American healthcare system.

In 401(k), the potential injury award was based on account balances that, in a bull market, might have been a couple of bucks higher if the plan selected brokers/funds/administrators that were better/cheaper/non-conflicted. Got that? The tort bar didn't see the beef either, so Wall Street was able to turn 401(k) fee disclosure into a total nothingburger. One way they did so was by sliding broker disclosures inside plan administrator disclosures. No kidding! Fidelity, for example, hid broker comp on the bottom of the left side of page 17 of their 23-page disclosure booklet. Yawn.

Fast forward ten years and it looks like the Department of Labor learned its lesson. This time, they made sure the Trump

---

6   U.S. Department of Labor Fact Sheet (2012) *Final Regulation Relating to Service Provider Disclosures Under Section 408(b)(2)*

Administration took the safety features off the torpedo by requiring that no service provider in the healthcare supply chain _BUT_ the broker provide the disclosure to clients.

In 2012, Momma Merrill, Fidelity, Schwab, et al. saved their conflicted brokers' keesters …during a bull market. But in 2021, after years of a healthcare premium "bear market", the statute ensures that there will be no hiding place on Page 17 for brokers because BlueCross, United, Aetna, and CIGNA are simply not involved. Brokers will be on their own. On their own to tell clients, probably for the first time, not only their base commissions, but also their add-on bonuses, overrides, persistency incentives, non-cash payments, trips to Cabo, and additional general agent compensation.[7]

When brokers mess this up, which they will, it triggers an ERISA breach that, again, exposes plan sponsors to personal liability. The potential monetary awards from healthcare lawsuits will be a skootch more enticing to the tort bar. Instead of the basis point dust on mutual fund fees, class action lawyers will sniff hundreds of millions in waste, fraud, and abuse suffered by angry Americans who hate a healthcare system because their costs rose by 275 percent over the twenty years employee wages grew by only 75 percent .

When we began our work to ameliorate 401(k) conflicts of interest in 1997, only five percent of Wall Street earnings were from fee-based business. Brokers charged everyone else $45 a trade. Today, those numbers have flipped. If you are under 40, you've never seen a TV commercial for a stockbroker. But you've seen plenty for fee-based planners sitting next to their customers touting, "We do well when our clients do well".

To survive in the post-fee disclosure world, and to check the "why you" box from CFOs and benefit committees, health insurance

---

7   Source: UnitedHealthCare Overview of Producer Compensation

brokers will need to do what Wall Street brokers did a decade ago: move their chairs to their clients' side of the table.

Why Change #1: A Penny Saved is Twelve Pennies Earned

If you have not been keeping up with the Kardashians, Kylie Jenner's lipstick business has seven employees and makes $600 million a year. Netflix makes $2.3 million per employee per year. These people don't care that Geico can save them 15 percent on their auto insurance and they sure don't care that health insurance premiums are going up 15 percent .

But down here at sea level, I talk to CFOs every day whose profits grow at five percent while their healthcare costs grow by 15 percent. That's not sustainable. The reflexive "we like our guy" or "talk to HR" goes away real quick when they figure out that healthcare costs crowd-out jobs, growth, and EBITDA.

The only feeling better to a CEO with 100 employees than finding five dollars in the back pocket of their jeans is freeing-up $250,000 of interest-free/tax free cash flow in their expense stack. Sure, they want to emerge from COVID and add a couple of sales-people, finance a new production line, or expand overseas. But at, say, a 10 percent margin, that requires $3 million in new pre-tax sales.

Now is the time to change from retail healthcare plans to insti-tutional plans because that interest free/tax free cash is just sitting in their SG&A back pocket waiting to be redeployed from healthcare waste, fraud, and abuse to far more productive projects.

Looking to sell your business in five years? Great. Let's say the M&A valuation in your industry is 10 times revenue. Now is the time to change from retail healthcare plans to institutional plans be-cause that $250,000 gives your exit package, when I went to school, a $2.5 million pop. The broker is a terrific guy and HR doesn't like change. Both seen as great reasons to justify staying put …but are they $2.5 million dollars great?

Why Change #2: Broker Fees vs. Results-Based Fees

Think about how you feel when the kid at Target tries to sell you an extended warranty on a $10 toy. Or the endless offers you get for identity theft protection. Or robocalls that have been "trying to reach you about your car's extended warranty". You probably felt that the salesperson stands to make money on something you probably don't need. As a former plan sponsor, that's how I felt when benefits brokers suggested we offer staff more and more policies, such as pet, eye glass, ransom (…no, seriously!), and hospital room insurance.

Quite the opposite when a consultant who gets a contingency fee on plan savings suggests a design upgrade. Since the consultant is a pig and not a chicken, the buyer trusts that any proposed changes are in the best interests of plan participants and their beneficiaries. They are about reducing the severity and frequency of claims, and not about a quick sale on a pet insurance policy. The client knows how much the contingency consultant is paid, and by whom. There is accountability and full transparency.

How It Works: Unscrewing the Lightbulb

OK, according to Weiss, the definition of a performance-based fee is money paid as equitable compensation for the value delivered. To get there, he suggests this formula to determine the return on investment on a value-based fee:

$$
\begin{aligned}
&\text{Tangible value} \\
\times\ &\text{Annualization} \\
+\ &\text{Intangible value} \\
\times\ &\text{Emotional impact} \\
+\ &\text{Peripheral benefits} \\
\hline
=\ &\text{ROI}
\end{aligned}
$$

Respectfully, I have absolutely no idea what that means and would never try to explain it to a third-generation manufacturer with 250 employees. So, regarding fees, here is the process we follow:

The Fiduciary Lightbulb Report

Firms in our core market of 50-500 employees have faced unsustainable rate increases of about 8.5 percent each year over the past decade, according to PwC's Health Research Institute. They don't know what they don't know, so our greatest value is to shine a light on the big lie that healthcare costs only go up. We want to shine that light on where they are, where they could be/should be, and provide fiduciary guidance to help them get there. And that's why our consulting program begins with…the Fiduciary Lightbulb Report.

The national average all-in per employee per year spend on healthcare is about $15,000. *Firms that follow their Lightbulb recommendations cut that in half.* References available upon request!

We begin with a fifteen-minute web call. If we think we can help, we generate a preliminary cost modeling analysis based on their census, renewal, and a few other things. We usually get approval to build a full report because the cash flow impact over time is often a number with two commas. To move forward with the final Lightbulb Report, we require a hard dollar fee of $3,000-$20,000. We charge a hard dollar fee to weed out those who are not serious. The fee is just cash flow timing because we contractually guarantee to return the money if the recommendations do not result in a 10x (there's that number again) reduction in plan costs.

The deal is that once they buy the Report, they can either tackle the recommendations themselves, turn it over to their incumbent broker to implement, or in select cases, we agree to replace the incumbent as advisor of record. If we do become the advisor of record, we refund the cost of the Fiduciary Lightbulb Report.

As their advisor of record, there are a whole lot of ways to structure things. If you are just waking up from the ERISA discussion, here's the Cliff Notes version: If we are massively successful, the client wins. If we are moderately successful, the client wins. If we are not successful, the client doesn't lose.

If, however, you were awake this whole time, here are the details: Instead of a $35 commission from the old broker, we often take a 40 percent haircut to keep our lightbulbs on. From there, we retain a share of savings. If we save the plan less than 10 percent of the pre-engagement spend, our bonus is zero. Our bonus kicks-in at a 10-20 percent savings. It goes higher at 20-30 percent savings, and caps out over 30 percent. If the original PEPY is relatively low, there is less work to be done so the savings share is lower than if we walk into a very high PEPY. Make sense?

And since you were about to ask, to free capital from the healthcare spend, here are a few categories in the toolbox, as noted by Health Rosetta.8 Are these well known to big box brokers and insurance carriers? You bet. Are brokers and carriers who make money as premiums go up going to tell you about them? Absolutely not!

- **Value-based primary care.** Properly conceptualized and incentivized primary care is the front line of defense against downstream costs.

- **Concierge services.** Navigating healthcare is complex, even for those of us in the industry. Employees need access to trusted, aligned resources.

- **Active ERISA plan management.** Employers deeply manage budgets in every other area of spend. Why not health benefits? Internal fiduciary oversight is critical.

---

8   Chase, David (2017) *The CEO's Guide to Restoring the American Dream.* Health Rosetta Publications.

- **Transparent medical markets.** Cost and quality are often inversely correlated. Focusing on better quality and outcomes is the path to lower costs.

- **Payment integrity.** Ensuring claims are paid correctly and tackling fraud is a critical step to high-performance benefits.

- **Transparent pharmacy benefits.** Purchasers need true transparency of data to control decision-making.

A Final Thought

I am told that benefits brokerage is a $22 billion industry and insurance companies are the source of the majority of that revenue. I've seen this movie before and believe that the next generation of health insurance brokers will pick up their chairs and join us on their clients' side of the table by adopting a compensation model driven by plan savings, not ever rising premiums.

It took economic and regulatory shocks for stockbrokers to become performance-based advisors and today, they do well when their clients' assets go up. The next generation of healthcare advisors will do well when their clients' costs go down.

…Everyone likes bacon.

Michael Case Smith

The Benefits Department

MIKE was on the frontlines of 401(k)'s massive reduction of conflicts and fees. Over the subsequent 20 years, healthcare costs went in the opposite direction. So today he applies proven processes to ameliorate conflicts, waste, and poor employee outcomes in group healthcare plans.

In addition to heading the agency, Mike is the Director of the Florida Manufacturers Healthcare Consortium. He began his career in the London and Los Angeles offices of a global pension advisor. In 1998 he and a group of colleagues joined Nobel Laureate Harry Markowitz to patent and license a series of financial technologies. In 2008, they purchased a New York investment firm. After a fivefold growth in assets, the company was sold, and Smith moved to Florida where he resides with his wife Karen and four (very) young children.

Smith has been a commentator for CNBC, MSNBC, The New York Times, and The Wall Street Journal. He is a vocal opponent of conflicts of interest on Wall Street, having testified before the Department of Labor, SEC, and the United States Senate. He has been a volunteer for Big Brothers, Los Angeles and Chicago prison mentoring programs, and Board member of Boys & Girls Clubs Chicago, Papua New Guinea US AID, Irish Georgian Society, and Notre Dame Club of Jacksonville.

CONTACT INFO —————————————————————

(904)-206-8642
msmith@benefits-department.com
www.benefits-department.com

14

The Critical Case for Evidence-Based Medicine

by Deborah Ault

WE ALL KNOW THE TYPE—the couple who is CONVINCED their fifth grader is going to the NBA! And what do those parents want as soon as their kid twists an ankle on the court? They want to see the local pro team's sports medicine physician and they want a CT scan of the ankle.

They have the noblest of intentions. They want the best possible care for their child.

What they DO NOT KNOW is that the local pro team's sports medicine physician is NOT an expert at pediatric sports injuries. A child's physiology is notably different from an adult's, especially in the skeletal system where children have numerous growth plates to support their development. A sports medicine doctor that works with a professional team is not used to dealing with those complications, which can lead to misdiagnosis.

They also do not know that the amount of radiation contained in a CT scan can be equivalent to the radiation of hundreds of plain film x-rays. Everybody knows that x-rays are dangerous…but nobody seems to understand that CT scans have far, far more radiation per scan. Nor are they aware of the increased risk of future development of cancer associated with the radiation exposure of CT Scans.[1]

Well, you're probably thinking, surely the physician will tell them all of that. But will they? A study shows that only ONE THIRD of patients were told by their doctors about the risks associated with a CT Scan.[2]

So, what's the solution to ensuring that your friend's child get the BEST possible care?

The answer is EVIDENCE-BASED MEDICINE!

What is evidence-based medicine?

The commonly accepted definition is "Evidence based medicine (EBM) is the conscientious, explicit, judicious and reasonable use of modern, best evidence in making decisions about the care of individual patients."[3]

The definition goes on to say that "EBM integrates clinical experience and patient values with the best available research information." This indicates that some degree of physician experience is added to the science, and that patient autonomy also has an impact.

If you keep reading, however, you will discover the third sentence: "It is a movement which aims to increase the use of high-quality clinical research in clinical decision making." And this is where patients, plan sponsors, and health plan advisors HAVE to pay attention!

You see, evidence-based medicine is NOT widely used or even widely accepted within the medical community! Oh, they will *tell* *you* that they practice EBM, but that's often not the case. Dr. Stacey

---

1   https://www.health.harvard.edu/cancer/radiation-risk-from-medical-imaging
2   https://www.reuters.com/article/us-doctors-ct-scan/doctors-dont-often-tell-patients-of-ct-scan-risks-idUSBRE92316120130304
3   https://www.ncbi.nlm.nih.gov/pmc/articles/PMC3789163/

Popko, MD, MBA, Managing Editor of MCG Health (the only in-dependent evidence-based medicine clinical criteria in the US) said, "I've never been to a cocktail party with a bunch of physicians and had any one of them say that they don't believe in evidence-based medicine. They all SAY they are doing it, but clearly that can't be the case — if it was, we wouldn't have the disparities in healthcare that we do."

The actual ACTIVE USE of evidence-based medicine, despite the fact that its entire existence is aimed at proactively and efficiently improving the health of patients, is still a "movement" in medi-cine — it is unfortunately NOT the standard practice.

Why is evidence-based medicine important?

In its simplest form, EBM details when the **benefits** of a particular procedure or service outweigh the **risks** associated with that proce-dure or service.

Using EBM helps a practitioner pick the procedures or ser-vices that lead to the best patient outcomes AND to do so in the most efficient way possible. We all recognize the merits of the best outcomes — everybody wants to be as healthy as possible. But let's take a second to examine what "in the most efficient way possible" means, shall we?

Why is efficiency in healthcare important? Well, from a patient perspective, no one wants to be fumbling around — taking time out of life to go to appointments and get procedures that lead to noth-ing beneficial. From an employer's perspective, they want everyone happy and healthy as quickly as possible for maximum productiv-ity. And, if the employer is also providing healthcare benefits for that patient, they CERTAINLY don't want a bunch of non-helpful procedures racking up bills. (Patients don't want unnecessary bills either; in fact, they are AFRAID of high medical bills, with about 40 percent of patients saying that paying for healthcare is scarier than being ill![4])

Why don't doctors use EBM?

Problem #1 — It's impossible to "keep up"!

As eloquently detailed in the chapter by Aaron Ault, medical knowledge is growing at an exponential rate, and keeping up is virtually impossible.

Problem #2 — Those who employ physicians are "not fans" of EBM.

Doctors are abandoning private practice to become employees of hospitals and health systems in record numbers.[5] In fact, the number of "employed physicians" now exceeds the number in private practice.[6] This is NOT good for patients, and in actuality, it isn't good for physicians either.[7] The stories employed physicians tell would scare the heartiest listener, but perhaps MOST telling is the fact that the number one thing that employed physicians like the least about their situation is the constraints imposed on their decision making.[8] As a patient and as a healthcare purchaser (that's YOU as an employer — since you are the one providing the coverage that pays for healthcare) you should read that as "your doctor is NOT free to make decisions without pressure from their employer." Hospital and health system administrators are generally NOT medical professionals, and their primary role is to "manage staff and budgets"[9] These

---

4   https://www.cnbc.com/2018/04/22/why-health-care-costs-are-making-consumers-more-afraid-of-medical-bills-than-an-actual-illness.html
5   https://www.healthcarefinancenews.com/news/doctors-leaving-private-practice-droves-joining-hospitals-report-says
6   https://www.ama-assn.org/about/research/employed-physicians-now-exceed-those-who-own-their-practices
7   https://www.medicaleconomics.com/view/employed-vs-independent-doctors-numbers-dont-tell-whole-story
8   https://www.medscape.com/slideshow/employed-doctors-6006080#8
9   https://www.betterteam.com/hospital-administrator-job-description#:~:text=Hospital%20administrators%20are%20responsible%20for,patient%20care%20amongst%20other%20duties.

are the folks responsible for employing physicians. Think about that for a minute!

Given that the goal of EBM is to make people healthier faster and to do so more efficiently, do you think those charged with managing the budgets of a fee-for-service healthcare delivery model have motivations aligned with EBM? EBM's goal is to get people healthier faster with the minimum number of procedures and services necessary to accomplish that. Hospitals and health systems are paid based on the number of procedures and services they perform. What would be the motivation for hospitals/health systems to perform FEWER and MORE EFFECTIVE procedures and services?

Problem #3 — The medical malpractice environment in the U.S.
Everyone knows that the US is litigious — there's even a joke about a man suing his mother for his birth being so traumatic. A KFF report from 2012 listed 13 primary drivers of healthcare spending, and medical malpractice was among them.[10] The fact of the matter is that physicians do NOT want to be sued for medical malpractice, so they have taken to prescribing based on what is termed "defensive medicine". How do I treat this patient without getting sued? And over 80 percent of them admit to doing it![11] In fact, one study showed that a PRIMARY way physicians avoid medical malpractice is by making patients happy via prescribing the medication that the patient specifically asks for — even if it is not what the physician would have chosen to prescribe if the patient had simply asked for something to treat their symptoms.[12] Remember our future NBA superstar — the one whose parents want a CT Scan? See why the physician might be willing to give them that CT scan without much discussion?

---

10   https://www.kff.org/wp-content/uploads/sites/2/2012/10/bpc_health_care_cost_drivers_brief_sept_2012.pdf

11   https://psnet.ahrq.gov/web-mm/defensive-medicine-glowing-pain

12   https://www.sciencedaily.com/releases/2014/03/140314111348.htm

Imagine if someone along the way had simply educated those parents about the risks and benefits of CT scans. What if someone coached them that they should let the physician do the examination, let the physician tell them what he thinks is best to prescribe, and then to ask questions rather than approaching the visit by walking in the door asking for what THEY (the parents) think they want? Better yet, what if someone had provided the parents with a resource that handed them the BEST care for their child (based on strong science) on a silver platter? What if they had been exposed, right at the point of illness/injury to EBM?

Many see technology as the solution to this problem. There are, however, some serious factors that we need to deal with. The biggest of them: There is no single "Consumer Reports" of healthcare that details the quality and cost considerations of healthcare services or the objective quality rankings of different providers. Fortunately, as of January 1, 2021 hospitals in the US are FINALLY legally required to publish their charge masters on line.[13] Unfortunately, as of this writing, only about one third are *actually* publishing their cost information,[14] and even amongst those some are taking active measures to prevent a normal person from being able to find the data.[15] Prior to the new law, even Americans who *wanted* to behave in a consumeristic fashion had no equipment to help them. Not only that, but the new law totally ignored the quality aspect!

Divorcing quality and cost is a grave error! Paying attention to one without regard to the other is not only lop-sided, but it is also a major part of what got us into this situation to start with. Even evidence-based clinical criteria do NOT address cost considerations.

13   https://www.cms.gov/hospital-price-transparency
14   https://www.wkyc.com/article/news/health/hospitals-ignoring-pricing-laws-surgery-procedures-health/95-83bacb90-1e3d-4c8f-83bb-c74a433b3492
15   https://www.wsj.com/articles/hospitals-hide-pricing-data-from-search-results-11616405402

Further, is it realistic to expect sick people/patients who very well may be in the most vulnerable position of their lives, to turn to tech for guidance? Even if we put the EBM information into the hands of every patient, would it be realistic to expect them to remember to "open the app" when the need strikes?

The only solution is independent medical care and utilization management. I believe so strongly in this solution that I built a company 19 years ago centered around it and I'm glad to see that it is finally making it into the "mainstream"!

I would even submit to you that if you really love the employees you are providing healthcare coverage for, then you have a duty and an obligation to bring them someone who can protect them at the most vulnerable times of their lives. That person needs to be clinical, to rely on science and evidence-based medicine, and they must be able to do basic math. Because, trust me, those things are grossly missing from our healthcare system in the US today. It also needs to be someone who won't be making their decisions based on emotion. You need someone with expertise at identifying those who might benefit from information about EBM. Someone who can put that information into the hands of parents so they can be an active participant in the decision making regarding their child's sports injury. Healthcare practitioners can't do it alone. Healthcare providers/health systems are demotivated from doing it by our current payment scheme. The ONLY person who can make a difference in this equation is the end-user: the PATIENT, and we have both a moral and ethical obligation to do all that we can to equip them with EBM. The best way to do this is to deploy a cutting-edge medical management strategy as a part of your health plan.

PS — If it is YOUR fifth-grader, RICE (Rest, Ice, Compression, Elevation), a plain film x-ray (which the right kind of telemedicine vendor can provide you an order for, and the right kind of carve-out imaging direct contract can get you for \$75 — including the radiologist reading fee!). If the x-ray is normal and the symptoms don't resolve after seven days, ask a physician about an MRI as a potential next step. See how easy having the right medical management makes things?

Deb Ault

Founder & President
Ault International Medical
Management

DEBORAH AULT (aka Nurse Deb) has been a Registered Nurse for thirty years. Before getting into Care Management, her bedside nursing experience included ER, ICU, Doctor's Office, Home Health, and Telephone Triage. Now she is the President of Ault International Medical Management (aka AIMM). Her team of nurses and doctors helps patients navigate both the health delivery and the health insurance systems. By ensuring that the right patients are getting the right care at the right time in the right place and at the right price, AIMM creates situations where the patient, provider, and plan all win! She is the author of 16 published outcome case studies as well as several editorials/articles and is a sought-after public speaker on these topics. Her passion and dedication to managed care has driven her success in the industry, saving employer-sponsored health plans countless dollars and improving the quality of patient care.

CONTACT INFO ─────────────────────────────────

Access a resource library from Deb and AIMM here:
https://nursedeb.lpages.co/book/

(866) 845-8854
www.aim-m.com

15

Turn Your Benefits into a Competitive Advantage

What your employees *believe*
about your benefits is more important
than the benefits themselves.

by Mark Holland

G OOD COMMUNICATION IS THE KEY to a successful business and satisfied employees. Many businesses, however, are challenged by the gap between what they spend on their benefits plan and employee *engagement* with the plan. According to the 2020 Economic News Release from the US Bureau of Labor and Statistics, the average company spends 30-40 percent in addition to payroll for employee benefits. Healthcare is usually a company's second largest operating expense after payroll. Yet, according to a 2019 consumer survey from Colonial Life, 69 percent of employees spend less than one hour annually considering their benefits.

Given the size of the benefits investment and the value employees place on benefits, companies and executives that prioritize employee communication and engagement around benefits will create a distinct competitive advantage for their businesses.

A Challenge for the C-Suite

Employees are a business' greatest asset and, as a C-suite executive, you should be thinking about how you can improve employee communication and engagement as it relates to your benefits plan. Ask yourself, "How important are my employees?"

Your benefits plan is a valuable tool that, when used to its full potential, can be a powerful link between employee and employer. By developing your plan as a competitive advantage, you can achieve your company's business objectives while simultaneously improving your employees' happiness at work and overall quality of life.

This may seem like a lofty goal, especially if you don't completely understand the ins and outs of the benefits industry yourself. But many of the basic business terms and practices commonly discussed in the C-suite can easily be applied to your benefits plan.

My business coach used to say, "Measure and monitor what matters," and this philosophy is entirely applicable to your benefits plan. In order to turn your plan into a strategic advantage, you should have S.M.A.R.T. (**S**pecific — **M**easurable — **A**chievable — **R**ealistic — **T**imely) goals clearly defined for your business. Ask yourself: What business objectives and strategic goals does our company have in relation to benefits spend? Are they written anywhere? What key performance indicators (KPIs) are measured against those goals? When was the last time you reviewed the business objectives for your benefits spend?

Once you have a firm understanding of your business objectives, ask yourself how your employees' understanding, awareness, knowledge, and appreciation for their benefits contribute to these goals. Communicating and engaging your employees in their benefits (particularly their healthcare benefits) generates a meaningful return on investment (ROI).

When we look at data, the numbers are compelling.

Attracting (And Keeping) Top Talent

Your benefits plan can be a powerful recruiting and retention tool and, in fact, you may want to use an onboarding survey to ask how the benefits offered by your company influenced your new employees' decision to join the team. Your recruitment and retention rates are a great KPI and, as an employer, you should be analyzing how your employees perceive your benefits plan.

Here's a true story about how my own team leveraged our benefits in a recent key recruitment: After a lengthy search and selection process for a new account manager, we made an offer to a candidate we were very eager to have join our team. But we learned that this prospective employee was going to reject our offer because the salary was lower than her current salary. Since we wanted to make this work, we engaged her in a deeper conversation on the topic of money — specifically about her current benefits and employee costs.

We were able to demonstrate that our benefits — which include a much lower deductible and out-of-pocket expenses as well as higher retirement contributions — are offered at a much lower cost to employees. So, although the salary we were offering was lower than her current pay, after factoring in our benefits costs, she realized our total package provided the equivalent of a raise, so she accepted our offer and joined the team. Yes, I could have simply offered a higher salary to close the deal, but being in the benefits business, I wanted to use this as a real-life test to see if this approach could make a difference. And it did.

While many of the KPIs in your company's marketing plan likely revolve around sales and revenue, employee retention and turnover should also be a KPI for your business, especially when you consider the effect they can have on prospective and current employees:

- **Recruiting** — Our account manager wasn't alone in understanding the value of employee benefits. The

American Institute of Certified Public Accountants (AICPA) found that 80 percent of employees would choose a job that offered them benefits over the same job that offered no benefits, even if that job offered a 30 percent higher salary. Consider how prospective employees might view your company's benefits plan not only as it impacts them, but also their dependents.

- **Retention** — A 2017 report from Work Institute estimates that replacing just one employee can cost 33 percent of their salary. In other words, if you lose one employee making the U.S. median salary of $45,000, you're likely to spend $15,000 in the process of finding and training a new hire. Imagine what else your company could do with that money if you use your benefits plan to increase your retention rates.

- **Morale** — Happiness is the key connector between benefits and employee productivity. The 17th Annual U.S. Employee Benefits Trends Study 2019 from MetLife revealed that "benefits customized to meet employee needs" are one of the top five drivers of happiness for employees. Combine that with the results of a study from Oxford University's Saïd Business School that found that happy workers are 13 percent more productive than their unhappy counterparts, and it's easy to see how better benefits can boost your bottom line.

Your business' benefits plan should be a sizable part of the recruiting and retention process. When employees search for a new job or decide whether or not to leave their current place of employment, they're thinking not only of themselves, but also of their dependents who are covered by their plan. If your workers know that they and their families are taken care of, they're much more likely to stick around and perform at their best.

The Role of HR

Employers often have their HR department or the CFO handle all the benefits decisions. In an era of evolving benefits, though, some business owners are now questioning how much control HR should really have over the company's benefits.

In my twenty-five years in this business I have been blessed to work with thousands of employer groups of all sizes from all over the country, and it's noticeable, even to an outside vendor, when the senior human resource officer has a seat at the table. When the chief human resources officer (CHRO) or VP of HR is one of the company's top five executives and recognized as a valued member of the senior leadership team (SLT), employee morale, attitude, and engagement are noticeably better.

If your mission is to focus efforts on your employees, the direct relationship between the CEO and the company's most senior human resource officer should be of the highest priority. From what I've seen, however, the CHRO and senior benefits managers rarely work closely enough with the CEO to capitalize on the true opportunities within their company's benefits plan. The current benefits decision maker(s) are often reluctant to break the status quo, fearing that changes without the C-suite buy-in could cause disruption and put their job security at risk.

In a more aligned system that allows a business to achieve its full potential, the CEO sets the vision, the CFO manages the finances, the COO runs operations, and the CHRO focuses on developing the people. We most often see benefits decisions and responsibilities flow up to the CFO due to the sheer size of benefits expenses, but your CEO should consider how each of these roles can maximize your plan's potential.

Understanding the value of your benefits plan and how it can be communicated into your overall business strategy is crucial for turning your plan into a competitive advantage. Employee understanding, satisfaction, and engagement should be KPIs that are considered in the company's goals and objectives, and although these goals should be part of the overall business objectives on the C-suite's radar, HR should lead the execution of the plan. Companies that do this well will achieve a competitive advantage over companies that do not.

It's time to think outside the box and reject the status quo. If we keep doing what we've always done, we will keep getting what we've always gotten. Companies that strike the right alignment with their senior leadership team will have a competitive advantage over those that don't properly distribute the responsibilities of their benefits plan.

Case Study: Betting on Benefits

A success story from one of our casino and hotel clients perfectly illustrates the power of communication. At the time, this client had about fourteen locations and 7,000 benefit-eligible employees. The goal was to improve employee engagement and increase employee understanding of the benefits offered while driving employees to consumerism regarding the health options and wellness programs.

The initial implementation took place at open enrollment, and it is worth noting that there were essentially no changes to the current benefits, employee costs, and providers for the year's open enrollment. The difference was the process.

The implementation included the rollout of a specific benefits brand, which involved a series of pre-communications through posters, e-mails, and management leading up to mandatory group and one-on-one meetings. Our process included:

- Coordinating the enrollment system buildout and enrollment logistics
- Delivering pre-enrollment communications through DVDs and HD-quality video group meetings (complete with presenters, interactive questions, and illustrative humorous skits)
- Hosting one-to-one enrollment meetings on-site at every location
- Utilizing laptops to capture enrollment, election, and beneficiary data.

Our company began managing the client's open enrollment and new-hire enrollment needs every month following the initial open enrollment. For the client's annual enrollment, we produced an interactive HD-quality video presentation of the new benefits brand for the employee benefits program and coordinated for every employee to attend a one-to-one enrollment session with an English or Spanish-speaking counselor. The client provided each employee with our pre-printed materials detailing the employee's enrollment options and costs.

Our company prepared the counselors with training regarding the branded benefit program and an enrollment system including existing benefits by employee, with associated costs, as well as all benefit options and the direct employee costs related to any open enrollment changes. Then, for a three-week period, each employee attended a pre-scheduled 30-minute one-on-one session with a benefits counselor to give all benefit-eligible employees the opportunity to get their specific individual benefits questions answered, verify all dependent and beneficiary information, and approve all elected coverage deductions.

Results That Speak for Themselves

The initiative to educate employees to be responsible consumers of healthcare and wellness initiatives led to higher participation, higher employee satisfaction and understanding, and clean data. In fact, more team members elected to participate in the higher deductible medical plan options. As an average for all locations, Plan 1 (the lowest deductible plan option) had a **42 percent decrease in participation**, Plan 3 (the highest deductible plan option) had a **46 percent increase in participation**, and Plan 2 (the middle deductible plan option) had a **13 percent increase in participation.**

Each employee had the opportunity to customize their benefits program to meet their specific needs. Through education and understanding of the potential indirect costs associated with an illness or accident, overall supplemental plan participation increased, with three supplemental plans seeing a **participation increase of 42 percent** compared to the previous year.

Here are some of the other impressive results from the investment into employee education:

- Voluntary short-term disability (STD) insurance participation increased by **18 percent** and voluntary long-term disability (LTD) insurance participation increased by **14 percent**.

- Voluntary life and dental insurance participation increased **4 percent**.

- Voluntary dependent life insurance participation increased by **24 percent**.

- Flexible spending account (FSA) participation increased by **2 percent**, with a **10 percent** increase in contributions.

The Stats of Satisfaction

Through a post-open-enrollment survey of nearly 3,000 employees, the client asked each employee to rank their preferred enrollment methods on a scale of 1 to 5 (with 1 being the lowest and 5 being the highest). When averaged across the company, the results were strongly favorable to personal one-on-one enrollment meetings.

The results were as follows:

- Personal One-on-One   4.4
- Human Resources   2.8
- Group Meeting   2.6
- Online   2.3
- By Phone   1.7
- By Mail   1.9

Our process of including knowledgeable counselors was also a critical factor in ensuring employee satisfaction, as the results of a survey of nearly 3,000 employees showed:

- Nearly **90 percent** ranked this year's open enrollment experience as very favorable.

- Nearly **95 percent** viewed the benefit enroller as very helpful in explaining the benefit package options and answering their questions.

- Employees did not feel pressured to make voluntary product elections.

- Almost **90 percent** strongly agreed the one-on-one enrollment experience was a productive use of their time.

Employees were more engaged with the employer and happy with the new process. They felt one-on-one meetings were a positive change, and an overwhelming majority wanted one-on-one benefits meetings in the future. The increased participation in every product line illustrates the employee's satisfaction and engagement.

Most of the products offered didn't have any employer contribution. When employers offer 100 percent employee-paid benefits and have low participation, there's a problem — either the employees don't understand what's being offered, or they don't *want* what's being offered, and it's almost always the former.

Lower costs are another hidden benefit of high employee participation. Most companies do a poor job of communicating benefits and, thus, insurance companies expect lower employee participation. The employees who *do* participate are likely to be the less healthy, higher-risk population, and because insurance companies charge based on risk, this can lead to higher costs for your employees and your business as a whole.

For our casino client, we went back to the insurance companies and had them re-rate the client while taking the new participation levels into consideration. By showing the better overall risk, we were able to convince the insurance company to lower their rates. Even better, the client was able to keep the same rate on several of the product lines for ten years. Yes, you read that right: the same rates over a ten-year span. Opportunity knocks!

The Path for Better Communication

If the key to a more effective benefits plan is better employee communication, then the key to better employee communication is a focus on accessibility. The easier it is for your employees and their families to find information and ask questions about their benefits plan, the more likely they will be to engage with their plan and deliver results that can create sizable savings for themselves and your business.

Technology can be a huge asset in this area, and the easiest way to get started is by developing a simple, easy-to-use website that employees can use to access all the relevant information for their benefits. The website should be accessible from any device and provide easy access to a downloadable and printable booklet that contains a summary of all available benefits, as well as a video presentation that offers an explanation of the benefits provided. Accessibility can be further improved by implementing a customized URL and mobile app. Remember that the goal isn't *only* to deliver information about your business' benefits, but also to help your employees understand how they can get the most out of their plan.

The use of video for better benefits communication is particularly effective. A study from the *Current Health Sciences Journal* revealed that, in the general population, 65 percent of people are visual learners while 30 percent are auditory learners. Incorporating video elements into your benefits communication strategy can help your employees retain more information about their plan. Remember also, that half the members on your healthcare plan are spouses and children rather than employees. Creating a CEO video introduction establishes an opportunity to enhance a personal connection with employees and their families. We've successfully implemented this with some of our clients. Go to our website resource page at the link provided at the end of the chapter to see examples and obtain copies of the scripts.

Don't rely on your website and pre-recorded videos for *all* your employee engagement, though. Open enrollment creates the perfect opportunity for personalized one-on-one discussions with both experienced and newly hired employees. While geography, size, and type of business can make this a logistical challenge, remote or traveling employees can still attend one-on-one meetings through web video conferencing apps like Zoom.

When communications are effective in regards to benefits, businesses truly experience better engagement, happier employees, and a significant ROI. But don't take our word for it—ask your staff. Employee surveys can show you how your workers want benefits to be delivered in the future, and to maximize participation, you can incorporate them into the open enrollment process along with mandatory one-on-one meetings. Doing this in our own benefits process allowed our employees to get the positive impact of the one-on-one experience while the company received plenty of employee feedback through the survey, allowing for future planning with the employees' perspective in mind.

The Winning Advantage

Don't underestimate the power of improving your benefits communication and employee engagement. Consider a review to make sure that your SLT's responsibilities and KPIs are properly aligned with your company's overall business plan and strategy. Companies that do this well will achieve a competitive advantage over companies that don't.

We are happy to share samples from the case study, additional materials, and even templates for the video and script of the CEO's message, the group meeting video, employee surveys, and the all-inclusive website. We are also happy to provide:

- More about this case and how we improved the risk to lower the costs

- Our whitepaper, *Communicating to Multi-Generational Populations*

- Our whitepaper, *3 Steps to Communicating Your Benefits More Effectively*

You can find these resources and more at:
https://benefithelp.com/2021bookresources

Mark Holland

CEO
BenefitHelp

MARK HOLLAND began his professional career as a small business owner at the age of 17. He later entered the insurance industry as an agent in 1994 gravitating to specializing in worksite marketing, benefit communication and electronic enrollment. Using his business and entrepreneurial skills, Mark became a founding partner and CEO of BenCom®. During this time, he managed the development of proprietary tools, processes and technologies that helped employers communicate and enroll their employee benefit programs. Over the years, these tools have been used by numerous national public companies, state governments and even major insurance carriers.

Mark is regularly recognized in national press and trade journals. He has been featured on CNBC and Bravo's World Business Review, Benefit News, Benefit and Compensation, as well as others. His newest venture, BenefitHelp™ is centered around an innovative approach in using the latest technologies to improve the healthcare and benefits industry. BenefitHelp™ has brought on several national customers and again introduced new technologies the marketplace.

CONTACT INFO —————————————————————
(901)-355-3500
MarkHolland@BenefitHelp.com
www.BenefitHelp.com

16

Control the Data & Win the Next Decade

by Ted Dixon

IRST, THE GOOD NEWS FOR employer sponsored group health plans. Like most other industries, the rapid expansion of technology and information is about to radically change this significant segment of your balance sheet. Take note of the new Transparency Laws being debated in Congress and the recently filed lawsuit by The Massachusetts Laborer's Health and Welfare Fund against Blue Cross and Blue Shield of MA. **Sunshine is about to be shed upon where and how your healthcare dollars are spent**. If you've paid attention to how this change has played out elsewhere in our society and economy, you will no doubt realize what it means for your company. Companies can access new and valuable information early on and implement strategies to harness this new data to provide your team with better healthcare at a lower cost than your competitor. The natural result will be their ability to more easily recruit and retain the best talent.

If you are the HR Director, CFO, COO or CEO of a private US business, large or small, you spend plenty of time grappling with the familiar issue of constantly rising healthcare premiums and declining levels of benefits. If you are in one of these positions you are likely smarter than the average bear, particularly when it comes to logic, emotional intelligence and creativity. Maybe you run a restaurant, car dealership, or a business with significant technology and/or shipping costs. Maybe you run several. It doesn't matter what business you are in, it is safe to assume you are acutely aware that you need to know every minute detail of every aspect of your operation. From man hours to toothpicks to the mark-up needed on used cars to turn a profit, you must have a handle on the cost items and how the whole supply chain works, and how to make the most of it. And if there are areas of the business you don't know enough about, you're smart enough to call in outside auditors on a regular basis to ensure the company isn't leaking unnecessary resources.

How do we check on these items? Data! In one form or another, you need reliable, unbiased data in order to inform your decisions moving forward. Yes, of course you do this to increase profitability, but for the vast majority of us, we do it to ensure that our business resources go to our most important asset. Our people!

Less than one percent of US businesses are publicly traded. I would argue that even those folks are very concerned about their people. For our purposes here, let's talk about the 99 plus percent that are privately held. It stands to reason that all of them are dedicated to the well-being of their employees. Even though you may be in the C-Suite of a larger company, you are one of the people. The C-Suite wants salaries to increase across the board for their people, and they are acutely aware that theirs will rise as well. You use data in any way you can to help achieve this.

However, when you go to the next notch down on your balance sheet, your healthcare-spend, you have a huge line item with little or very opaque data associated with it. Most of us entrust all of the data to one of five huge publicly traded organizations; Blue Cross, United, Cigna, Aetna and Humana. From some of the very largest self-funded plans like the aforementioned Massachusetts Laborer's Health and Welfare Fund down to a small, five person fully insured group, these folks DO NOT want you to 'see behind the curtain'. Between the passing of The Affordable Care Act and today, these large insurance companies' stock prices have increased between 200 and 400 percent. In that same period the cost of healthcare to you and your employees has doubled. Has the value of your business quadrupled in that time? Have employee salaries doubled? Where would you be now if you had doubled prices to your market since 2010 while offering reduced services?

The US healthcare system is stacked against you and your employees and all working Americans. Our medical facilities operate at cost when they bill Medicare, or at a loss when they bill Medicaid. Where do they make up for this in order to grow their business in the form of research, salaries, buildings and ever-expanding middle management? Three guesses, and the first two don't count. Does the Health Insurance company you contract with each year concern themselves with your ever-expanding premiums? Why would they?

How did we get here? We all got complacent. Medical providers and facilities are happy to have opaque pricing. Health insurance carriers keep a defined portion of your premium dollars and aren't too concerned about raising them slightly (or significantly) each year. As your broker/consultant, it is easy for us to present you with a spreadsheet each year to compare all the carriers that pay us the same and bonus us when they accumulate a sizable portion of our business. But wait, you don't get a free pass either! I'm not going to claim it's easy, but the straightest path for you is to select your carrier, pick a plan design from their shelf, and get open enrollment done and over with.

So, how much does this cost? According to a Kaiser Health survey done in 2019, the average total premium dollars per employee per year for an American business was $13,500. Look familiar? If we all continue to bury our head in the sand, that number will climb to $26,664 per employee per year by the end of this decade. This is based on a six percent year over year increase. I don't know about your broker, but when I deliver a client a six percent increase, I typically say, "Well, in the grand scheme of things, that's not so bad".

Really? Are you kidding me?! Well, no, really, I am not BS'ing you when I say that. Because for you and I at renewal time the 'grand scheme of things' is the next twelve months. You are happy to not have to announce a change in carrier to your employees and get on with what you do best. Your business. I am happy to call the office, tell them that you'll stay put and peel out of your parking lot for lunch, never to be seen again until next year. See how it gets pretty comfy for all of us involved?

You probably wouldn't let any other consultant that your business engages with off the hook so easily. But don't beat yourself up on this one. We do business this way because there is no way for me to really explain what it is you are getting for your $13,500 per employee. We may be able to discuss your premium to claims ratio or even get some high claimant data. That usually just informs us whether we should go to market or start an HRA. Same old song and dance, but we've covered ourselves for the next twelve months.

I would like to propose that you and I stop looking at this as a 12-month grand scheme of things and start planning three, five and ten years down the road. It is a heavier lift for both of us, but can you afford the alternative? Some might be able to and some might have to. The employers that lead the way in using data made available by cutting edge technologies will hire and retain the best talent over the next decade. Is there any argument that this will be the secret sauce to success?

So, how do you access the data to both offer improve health benefits and also lower premiums? Do you think your insurance company is going to help by providing you with the full data picture? Fat chance! But t here are new information technologies available today in 2021 that were not even a twinkle in someone's eye in 2019. Now you and I can really make a thirty-six month plan using actual data. No more guessing!

Here are three concrete examples of how a company of any size can leverage today's technology to build a group health plan that their competitors never dreamed of so that they become the ones attracting and retaining the best talent in their market.

Let's look at a 5-life group health plan currently fully-insured with United.

- First, we use Enlighten Analytics or Rover Analytics to build a spot-on report of claims over the last 24 months. This simply requires the employees to log into their United Portal. These two technologies provide us with data that United wouldn't even know how to extract.

- Next, we will use this data to inform how we design a plan with someone like Benefit Indemnity Corporation. We will know exactly what strategies to implement in order to give your employees a plan with concierge medical and pharmacy guidance, zero-dollar deductibles and no co-pays.

Now let's take a 400-life group also fully-insured with United. They get some large claimant data each year that United uses to scare the heart out of them and justify ever increasing premiums.

- First, we use the Verikai Predictive Risk tool using 400 public data points that allow us to see exactly what your

group's claims risk truly is. We won't even bother your
employees with this, we use a member level census.

- We use this data to custom tailor a plan using the
appropriate strategies and tools.

- Next, we partner with a real time data tool like The Health
Care Command Center provided by Trifecta Health
Solutions. This independent watchdog tracking your data
constantly and at the same time suggesting solutions is not
your grandfather's 'Auto Claims Adjudication'! No cozy
payor/provider relationship here. This is true payment
integrity which you and your employees deserve for such a
critical expenditure.

Now let's look at a multiple thousand life case that is already
using an insurance company for Administrative Services Only.
Logic tells us they have loads of data at their fingertips they can use
to both enhance their plan and control costs. Not necessarily the
case. A lawsuit filed by The Massachusetts Laborers' Health And
Welfare Fund against their Administrator, Blue Cross Blue Shield
Of Massachusetts, filed on March 26, 2021 is filled with nuggets
that amplify the lack of data even our largest plans have had access
to. Even the 'Agreed Upon Facts' highlighted in this lawsuit will
make your hair catch fire considering the long-lasting relationship
of trust between these parties. The disagreement says it all. The employer says it wants their own data and the administrator says no.
Really??!!! This is a huge union that deducts big money from each of
their employee's paychecks every hour and hands it to Blue Cross to
ensure their health and welfare is top notch. And when they ask to
see the details of how this money is spent, Blue Cross says no! This
clearly indicates we **_ALL HAVE A BIG PROBLEM._**

The solution, even for a plan this size? Unfettered access and auditing of the data. The same tools that are used in so many other industries are now available to Employer Sponsored Health Plans.

- In this instance The Massachusetts Laborers' Health And Welfare Fund is employing an independent payment integrity partner to examine both past and present claims. They will be able to use this information to:

  1) Retrieve 'overspend' from the last 24 months

  2) Use the data to better inform decisions moving forward in order to provide better benefits at a lower cost for their members

It is mind-boggling that their long-trusted payor has forced them to sue in order to achieve this.

What does an Employer Sponsored Health Plan look like when they demand vision of and control over each piece of data along the healthcare supply chain? I give you Rosen Hotels & Resorts based in Orlando Florida. The first thing that may jump out at you about their healthcare plan is that it costs them a full 45 percent less per employee per year ($7500) than the national average. Must be because they saddle their employees with huge co-pays and deductibles, right? Wrong! Rosen employees have no co-pays or deductibles on their plan and they enjoy concierge medical care. It gets better. Rosen takes the savings they achieve on their healthcare spend and pays for college for their employees' children.

Rosen Hotels & Resorts is thriving in a highly competitive industry in perhaps the most competitive part of the world. Their 'secret sauce'? A 90 percent employee retention rate. You can't automate hospitality.

Where will employee retention rank for your company in a post-pandemic world? Where will you find the resources to pay your employees a competitive salary and benefits? Do you think the employers that learn earlier rather than later that data is important to their healthcare spend and therefore their entire existence will have a competitive advantage?

Demand the data. It is now available. Even though Rosen Hotels & Resorts are a model of employee benefits and thus retention, they continue to demand better data. They are actively searching for solutions like Trifecta's Health Care Command Center. Your plan now has access to the same. Demand it and you will be on the winning side of the next decade.

Ted Dixon

CEO
Dixon Associates

TED DIXON is the CEO of Dixon Associates and brings a uniquely powerful background to the company. Immediately after graduating from Bates College in 1990, he went onto pursue a master's degree from The United States Sports Academy which led to his first career as a coach and administrator at the collegiate level. His passion for business drove him to take the leadership skills developed coaching collegiate athletes into the business world at two successful startups, before joining Dixon Associates in 2003.

Today, as the CEO of Dixon Associates, Ted provides the vision and leadership for his team while keeping a close eye on the value, they are providing each client they serve. Through strategic partnering, Dixon Associates helps clients return money from their healthcare spend to their employee's pockets.

CONTACT INFO

Connect with Ted on LinkedIn at:
www.linkedin.com/in/teddixon1
(781)-934-0648 ext: 304
ted@dixon-associates.com
www.dixon-associates.com

459 Washington St. #26
Duxbury, MA 02331

17

Healthcare's Great Transformation

by Robin Flaherty

THE PANDEMIC FORCED EVERY PERSON, company, and industry to reassess what they do and how they do it. Life as we knew it has changed and transformed. Yet, many 'great' and consequential events have fixed their place in history. In healthcare, the Great Transformation is being brought about by the confluence of an unsustainable cost trajectory, pricing transparency laws, and emerging, restorative fixes to the healthcare supply chain. These things are reshuffling the deck, and the invisible hand of the market is shifting the power from the classes to the masses. Healthcare's Great Transformation belongs to the consumer—and here's how employers can take what is rightfully theirs: Control.

It's a health plan, not a health guess

It's customary to call a health insurance policy a 'health plan', but many employers do not have the luxury of planning because they lack the claims information needed to plan. Before you can use your claims information as a strategic asset, you must first acquire it. Even if you think you are getting your data, I suspect many companies are not getting a level of claims detail that is actionable.

This chapter is for employers who are interested in the positive attributes of change that having your healthcare claims data will provide not only your company, but your employees, their family members, and ultimately, your community. When your company saves money with using their claims data to optimize the structure and management of your health plan, the money saved can be better spent on increased wages, lower employee health insurance contributions, or business expansion—all changes that will positively impact your community. The journey to better your company and impact your community starts with obtaining the right healthcare claims data.

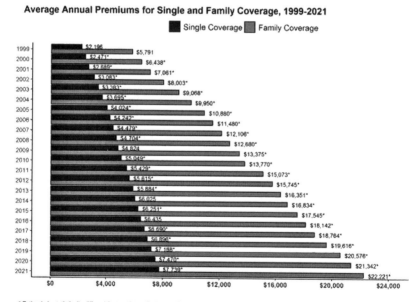

Average Annual Premiums for Single and Family Coverage, 1999-2021

* Estimate is statistically different from estimate for the previous year shown (p < .05).
SOURCE: KFF Employer Health Benefits Survey, 2018-2021; Kaiser/HRET Survey of Employer-Sponsored Health Benefits, 1999-2017

Having access to your claims data is the difference between controlling your expense or continuing to be subject to the health insurance premium increases that the current system dictates—and in the past 22 years, the system has dictated single and family premium increases of 252% and 284%, respectively. How do you take back control of an expense that, in any other category on the income statement, would undergo much scrutiny, oversight and strategic planning? Know the frequency and occurrence of claims on a level of detail that allows you to manage this expense category that ranks # 2 or # 3 on your income statement.

Whether your company's health plan is fully insured or self-funded, your claims data is pivotal as it will ultimately determine your ability to guide the various ways you can control your overall healthcare spend. In other words, be in control or be controlled.

Before I go any further, I want to be clear that I am criticizing practices, not people. In my 24 years in the employee benefits industry, I have met hundreds of wonderful, very well-meaning people in every capacity of the supply chain—it's just that there's an acceptance that one line item on your income statement, and one of the largest, can't be managed. If you get nothing else from this chapter, consider that one simple rule of business: "If you pay, you should have a say" applies to healthcare, too.

If you currently do not have actionable claims data from your healthcare spend, the reasons can range from a simple not asking the right questions to a more complicated reason, such as your health carrier claims to own the claims data and is unwilling to share at a level that provides you with enough information so you can question their decisions in regards to managing your spend. To further complicate the claims acquisition issue, the insurer, as the claims administrator and the party with the financial risk, is typically deemed the primary "owner of claims data." As a covered entity under HIPAA, the insurer is restricted regarding the circumstances under which it can share claims information with the employer, and as a business with a profit motive, the insurer is often reluctant to share that data with the employer for other reasons. Nonetheless, ERISA places on the "Plan Administrator," which is typically the employer (or a group of employees designated by the employer), a fiduciary duty to oversee the insurer and ensure that its actions are prudent and taken in the best interests of plan participants and fiduciaries (your employees). The Plan Administrator has an obligation to act as a safeguard to assure that plan assets are protected, used prudently, and delivered in the best interests of the plan members. There are compelling arguments that employers need to protect themselves and take a proactive approach to being a best-interest fiduciary of the assets that plan members are contributing (i.e., employee contributions for their share of premiums), but employers are finding it difficult to fulfill their obligation in the absence of access to claims data. Sure, employers believe they are doing their best to design the best-interest health plan, but without data, it's a guess.

Data is also a key element in the determination if self-funding is right for your company, and to provide you with a negotiating position at renewal. If you do not have access to your claims data, modern risk assessments use vast amounts of consumer data and can create a risk profile for your population to further assess if self-funding is right for your company.

You can't manage what you can't measure

The Affordable Care Act gave authority to the states to redefine small group as 1–100 employees and depending on the number of employees your company has, and the state where your business was incorporated, you may have some restrictions on self-funding. For example, in New York it is prohibited to sell stop loss insurance in the small group (1–100 employee) market.

The remainder of this chapter focuses on large groups (100+ employees) that should have access to their claims data for the asking, as the larger the company, the more influence to be wielded at the healthcare claims data negotiating table (in a perfect world). Companies have more power than they realize, and tools exist today to empower you to take control of your total healthcare spend. It's cliché, but true: Knowledge is power, and you can't manage what you can't measure.

When You Know:

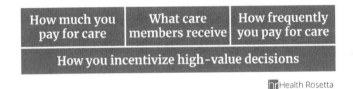

Health Rosetta

You will be able to take control of your healthcare spend.

Healthcare Claims Needed & Why

Claims Data Category	Importance
Medical claims paid by diagnostic category, providers & facilities	This will tell you how much you spend for healthcare and where the money is spent. Historical data will identify patterns and trends to interrupt the occurrence and frequency of claims, where possible. You will also want to benchmark the care venue to ensure it's a high value one. Health analytic software programs are available to compare your claims data with a larger population to interpret and identify risks of undiagnosed health issues so you can be proactive and build wellness and other intervention programs to support your at-risk populations.
Prescription drug claims detailed by specific drug and pharmacy	Pharmacy Benefits Managers (PBMs) that are not carrier embedded may be the most cost effective. Transparent PBMs work on a fixed fee vs. per fill cost. Drug rebates from the pharmaceutical companies need to be disclosed and returned to your company.
Members using in network & out of network providers, facilities and pharmacies	To identify and set contracts with providers, facilities and pharmacies with the highest value of care and the best cost.
Members Utilizing Wellness and Preventive Care Benefits	To identify educational programs that engage and incentivize members to maintain and protect their health.
Denied Claims	Identify claim problems early and protect both your employees and your company from cost uncertainties.

Reasons for not having actionable healthcare claims data:

1. Told by their insurance carrier, "We can't release that information due to HIPAA". Not so. The Health Insurance Portability & Accountability Act of 1996 was enacted to ensure the proper protection and proper dissemination of Protected Health Information (PHI), not the withholding of PHI. There's a process to ensure that PHI only makes it into the hands of those authorized to receive it, and those hands include those employees of the employer who are responsible for health plan administration and operations. HIPAA provides alternative procedures to allow for data share after de-identification—but HIPAA was never enacted to block the free flow of information between insurers and Plan Administrators. See the next section for a general overview of the HIPAA requirements and process by which employers can get more extensive claims data (which includes PHI) from their insurers.

2. "Our system can't extract that information". Again, nope. There are over 10,000 medical Current Procedural Terminology (CPT) codes that need to be acknowledged in a given database for billing purposes, so logic tells you that despite the sophistication of any system, if the system provides codes for billing, it can provide reporting out of what was billed. Data warehouse software systems exist that take raw data claim feeds and create meaningful intelligence that, coupled with the right claim mitigation vendors, provides the tools to manage your expense.

3. Information that is too general leads to confusion as to what data details would help manage the expense. The list of claims data categories needed, and why, in this chapter are meant to serve as a field guide as you begin your journey.

4. Unaware that such information is available for the asking.

PHI is crucial as it is the underlying data that can help employers make informed decisions as to their plan design and which strategic levers to use to manage their expense. If you meet resistance, push. Dig deeper and demand the information you need to provide the proper fiscal oversight to this top three business expense.

I will leave you with this thought as you consider your rights to your healthcare claims data if you are initially or continually denied access: *What vendor, if they were proud of their work for you, would withhold information?*

How Employers Can Get PHI from Their Insurers[1]

The type of claims data most useful to employers will typically involve PHI. While virtually every self-insured plan needs (and likely already has) access to PHI to administer the plan, fully-insured plans may not have access to PHI. To get access to PHI, employers generally need to make changes to their governing documents and operations. Those changes are required by HIPAA and are summarized below.

First, the employer's health plan document must be amended to comply with HIPAA's privacy and security rules. This amendment includes several components:

A. The amendment must define the permitted and required uses of disclosures of PHI by the employer. 45 CFR §164.504(f)(2)(i). All uses of PHI are limited to "plan administration functions" performed by the employer. 45 CFR §164.504(f)(3)(i).

---

1 Nothing in this chapter should be viewed as legal advice. Particularly with respect to HIPAA, I encourage you to consult with legal counsel about an employer's rights and obligations regarding PHI and the required documentation to enable you to handle PHI properly. Your benefit advisor can facilitate the process with an ERISA attorney.

B. The amendment must provide that the plan will disclose PHI to the employer only after the plan receives the employer's written certification that the plan documents have been amended as required by HIPAA, and that the employer agrees to the various restrictions in the amendment (such as not using or disclosing PHI for employment-related actions). 45 CFR §164.504(f)(2)(ii).

C. The amendment must provide for adequate separation (a "firewall") between employees of the employer who will have access to PHI to perform plan administration functions, and all other employees who will not perform such functions. 45 CFR §164.504(f)(2)(iii). This requires designating specific employees who need access to PHI, restricting their access to the plan administration functions the employer performs for the plan, and providing a mechanism to address such employees' non-permitted uses and disclosures of PHI. 45 CFR §164.504(f)(2)(iii).

D. If the employer will have access to electronic PHI, the amendment must require the employer to (i) implement administrative, physical, and technical safeguards to protect PHI; (ii) ensure that the privacy firewall is supported by appropriate security measures; (iii) ensure that any agent or subcontractor who receives PHI implements appropriate security measures to protect the PHI; and (iv) report security incidents. 45 CFR §164.314(b)(2). Because almost all PHI is electronic now, these changes will be required for most employers.

Second, the employer must certify to the health plan, in writing, that the employer has amended the health plan document and agrees to the restrictions in the plan amendment. 45 CFR §164.504(f)(2)(ii). In other words, the certification is the key that unlocks the employer's access to PHI. Although the insurer cannot share PHI with the employer until it receives the employer's certification, most insurance companies have such certification forms at the ready. With such access, the employer becomes "hands-on" with respect to PHI, and therefore must comply with additional requirements under HIPAA's privacy and security rules, as further described below.

To comply with those rules, the employer must adopt HIPAA policies and procedures to govern the uses, disclosure, and protection of PHI. 45 CFR §164.308; 45 CFR §164.530. A detailed description of what is required is beyond the scope of this chapter. However, by way of example, the employer's policies and procedures must appoint a HIPAA privacy officer, provide for employee training on the privacy rules, and establish administrative, physical, and technical safeguards to protect PHI. 45 CFR §164.530(a)(1); 45 CFR §164.530(b)(1); 45 CFR §164.530(c)(1).

Further, the employer will need to develop and maintain a separate "notice of privacy practices" that is distributed to plan participants, posted on the employer's benefits website, and available to plan participants upon request. 45 CFR §164.520(a)(2)(ii). The notice must describe the employer's uses and disclosures of PHI and participants' rights, such as the right to inspect, amend, request additional restrictions on, and receive an accounting of disclosures of a participant's PHI. 45 CFR §164.520(b)(1)(iv).

An Alternative Perspective on Claims

Now that we have discussed why getting your healthcare claims data is important, let's look at an alternative assessment of where your claim dollars go…

According to AHIP, America's Health Insurance Plans (the national association of private US health insurers), "here is where your premium—how much you pay for your health insurance coverage each month—helps cover the costs of the medications and care you receive and improves healthcare affordability, access and quality for everyone. Here is where your healthcare dollar really goes."

Posted by AHIP on November 12, 2020:

21.5¢	19¢	19.8¢	3.2¢	12.1¢	6¢
Prescription Drugs	In-Patient Hospital Costs	Out-Patient Hospital Costs	Emergency Room Costs	Doctor Visits	Other Out-Patient Care

4.6¢	3.1¢	2.4¢	0.8¢	4.4¢	3¢
Taxes and Fees	Other Fees and Business Expenses	Cost Containment	Quality Improvement	Other Administrative Expenses	Profit

This data represents how commercial health plans spend your premiums. This data includes employer-provided coverage as well as coverage you purchase on your own. Data reflects averages for the 2016–18 benefit years. Percentages do not add up to 100% due to rounding.

While this graphic depicts a general understanding of where a healthcare dollar "really goes" (my emphasis), clearly, it's more meaningful for each employer to know where *their* healthcare dollars are spent so that they can be the judge of whether or not the spend was value-based. This graphic is based on volume, not value—there's a difference.

Pricing Transparency: President Trump's Healthcare Legacy

President Trump issued an Executive Order in June 2019 demanding transparent prices in healthcare (https://www.nytimes.com/2019/06/24/upshot/health-care-price-transparency-trump.html). In November 2019, the Centers for Medicare and Medicaid

Services (CMS) issued a final rule requiring hospitals to post clear, accessible pricing information online (Hospital Price Transparency Rule), beginning January 1, 2021. 84 Fed. Red. 65,524 (Nov. 29, 2019). The American Hospital Association filed a lawsuit in December 2019 to keep prices secret and lost on Tuesday, June 23, 2020 (https://www.nytimes.com/2020/06/23/upshot/hospitals-lost-price-transparency-lawsuit.html).

Various federal agencies have stepped up efforts to increase transparency in healthcare. In November 2020, the Internal Revenue Service, Employee Benefits Security Administration, and CMS issued final rules requiring group health plans and health insurers to provide participants (via website or paper form) with cost-sharing information upon request, including an estimate of the individual's cost-share for items or services provided by a particular provider. 85 Fed. Reg. 72,158 (Nov. 11, 2020). This change takes effect for plan years beginning on or after January 1, 2023. The final rules also require plans and insurers to disclose in-network provider negotiated rates, historical out-of-network allowed amounts, and drug-pricing information through a website so the public can understand healthcare pricing. This change takes effect for plan years beginning on or after January 1, 2022.

In the same vein, the Consolidated Appropriations Act, signed in late December 2020, requires health plans and insurers to provide advance explanations of benefits (EOBs) and online price comparison tools to allow patients to estimate the cost of different items and services. Pub. L. No. 116-260. These changes, which are separate from those discussed in the final rules above, take effect for plan years beginning on or after January 1, 2022.

In July 2021, CMS announced that hospital compliance with the Hospital Price Transparency Rule has been sporadic and to increase compliance, proposed modifications to the Civil Monetary Penalties

(CMP) that is set to take effect January 1, 2022. Unfortunately, many believe that the CMPs are set at a level that are less than what the hospitals have to lose if they are forced to be transparent.

I believe that consumers (both employers and employees) should use the growing momentum towards health pricing transparency as a watershed moment to demand full transparency from all vendors in their healthcare supply chain (whether fully-insured or self-funded). Not only will transparency provide you with the fiscal oversight of your top three business expense needs, it may help protect you from fiduciary duty claims under ERISA.

For updates on the developing price transparency laws, visit my website at www.benefitlink.net.

Who cares the most, wins

The business origin story that inspires me the most is from Sara Blakely (founder of Spanx): Rather than be intimidated by the established, status quo system of the hosiery manufacturing industry that existed 20 years ago, she said to herself, "I don't have the most experience, I don't have the most money, but I do care the most. And let me see what happens if I care the most". Caring the most worked out for Sara Blakely and I know it will work out for the employers and employees that care the most about the cost of their healthcare and work to understand how they can affect change for not only themselves, but their employees and community.

What's Next

My professional goal is to convene the healthcare consumer audience in Rochester, New York and lead employers and employees to create a Rochester Community Health Fund that is owned and controlled by those who pay for and use healthcare. I know that sounds ambitious, but "Never doubt that a small group of thoughtful, committed citizens can change the world; indeed, it is the only thing that ever has". (Margaret Mead)

When I heard Dave Chase, Founder of Health Rosetta (www. healthrosetta.org) speak at the World Healthcare Congress in April of 2018, I knew I had found a group of committed citizens who are changing the healthcare world. Health Rosetta's tagline says it all: "Healthcare is already fixed. Join us to replicate the fixes". Doesn't that make you want to know how they have fixed healthcare? Premiums keep rising double digits and most employers in my hometown are completely in the dark as to their healthcare claims and the power that comes from knowing such information. I believe that employers reading this who think they are getting a complete look at their claims information could be getting an even more granular view in order to take action and consider vendors outside of a carrier supply chain to identify stacks of hidden profit.

Final Thoughts

I am so fortunate to have built relationships with many talented professionals around the country who are mission-aligned to solve healthcare for the consumer in their region and share best practices. The cost containment strategies I learned from Health Rosetta, Mitigate Partners and the NextGen Mastermind provide proof of concept with an impressive collection of employer case studies that I am happy to share with any employer who is concerned about their ability to pay for healthcare, curious how another employer's success with managing healthcare might apply to them, and optimistic that healthcare's great transformation will provide them with the tools and transparency laws they need to be successful with managing their spend. The only barrier to your success will be obtaining your healthcare claims data—and don't be bashful about demanding it! If your request for your claims information is denied, or your insurance carrier doesn't say yes, but doesn't say no, keep pushing (with this field guide as your reference), and if you get nowhere and feel powerless, **please remember who writes the check!**

Robin Flaherty

Founder & President
Benefit Link

ROBIN FLAHERTY started consulting in the employee benefits industry in 1997 after a career as a CPA in the tax department at Coopers & Lybrand (now PricewaterhouseCoopers).

Robin leads Benefit Link, an employee benefit consulting company that advises employers who have strategic options for using their claims data to aggressively manage affordable, high-quality healthcare for their employees. Benefit Link also helps employers and employees take the guesswork out of selecting health insurance plans for companies with less than 100 employees. As part of her employee benefit consulting client work, Robin is a thought leader on the budding disruptions in healthcare and advises companies that are transforming how healthcare is purchased and delivered.

CONTACT INFO ———————————————————————

(585)-349-8000
robin@benefitlink.net
www.BenefitLink.net

18

Life and Death at the Drug Store

by Daniel LaBroad

WHEN ALEC SMITH TURNED 26 IN 2017, he dropped off his parents' health insurance plan. Normally that's not a big deal, but Alec was diabetic and the insulin he got for free under his parents' plan, now cost him a whopping $1300 per month. Alec did have the opportunity to enroll in his own employer's health plan. However, while his restaurant manager salary of $35,000 a year was enough to live on, it certainly wasn't enough for him to also afford the insulin costs under his new health plan. Yet, his salary was high enough that he didn't qualify for medical assistance from the state.

Unable to afford his insulin, Alec began rationing it, hoping to reduce the monthly cost while still staying medicated. Alec's plan didn't work, and ultimately yielded tragic results because he didn't get enough insulin. He died.

Like many employees in the US, Alec was enrolled in a typical high-deductible, high monthly premium healthcare plan, the kind that most cost-conscious employers opt for. In those plans, chosen for their affordability, prescription drugs are often expensive, and prescription drug benefits don't kick in until the insured meets the plan's out-of-pocket deductible, which can run as high as $10,000 (Alec's deductible was $7,600, and his monthly plan premium was $450). As a result, employees must bear the brunt of rising prescription drug costs, which can be dramatic. For instance, Eli Lilly's per-dose price of insulin in the US has gone from $35 in 2001 to $235 in 2015, which is a 585 percent jump. Also, between 2015 and 2020, the annual price of Victoza, another diabetes medication, increased by 42 percent, with the price of a year's supply rising from $7,936 to $11,300.

Because of his changed health plan and situation, Alex was unable to afford life-preserving medicine and he suffered the consequences. In keeping with the theme of this book, it's not an overstatement to say that decisions made about healthcare coverage, especially company prescription drug plans, can have life-and-death consequences.

A big, nationwide problem

Nearly half (approximately 45 percent, or 133 million) of all Americans suffer from at least one chronic disease and the number is growing. Chronic diseases—including, cancer, diabetes, hypertension, stroke, heart disease, respiratory diseases, arthritis, obesity, and oral diseases—can lead to hospitalization, long-term disability, reduced quality of life, and death. In fact, persistent conditions are the nation's leading cause of death and disability. People who are being treated for persistent conditions almost always require regular prescription medications. It's also no secret that people in the US are paying more and more every year for less and less healthcare, especially for their prescription drugs. Prescription drug spending in the US has increased 50 percent in the past decade, now up to

$328 billion, and it is expected that Americans will fill 4.98 billion prescriptions annually by 2025.

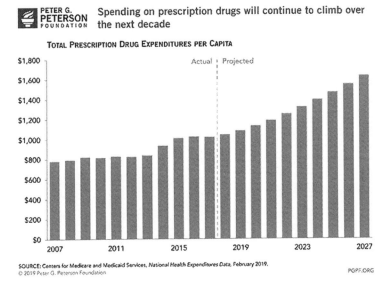

PETER G. PETERSON FOUNDATION — Spending on prescription drugs will continue to climb over the next decade

TOTAL PRESCRIPTION DRUG EXPENDITURES PER CAPITA

SOURCE: Centers for Medicare and Medicaid Services, National Health Expenditures Data, February 2019.
© 2019 Peter G. Peterson Foundation   PGPF.ORG

A survey conducted by GoodRx in 2018 found that about one-third of Americans admitted they have skipped filling a prescription one or more times because of cost. And according to an online flash poll of over 1,000 U.S. adults conducted by PawnGuru, an online marketplace that conducts regular surveys, 44 percent of respondents said that within the last year they did not purchase at least one medically necessary prescription because of cost. Also from that study, 20 percent of respondents say they're currently paying more than $100 a month out of pocket for their prescriptions. And 40 percent of those surveyed say their insurer has declined to cover a prescription at least once in the past year.

How would you feel if you found out that your employee became critically ill, or even died, because they could not get their required medications due to limitations you approved of in your health plan?

There are about 125,000 U.S. deaths per year due to medication non-adherence. When employees don't adhere to their medications, they tend to increase your healthcare spending because they now need more expensive treatments and care as opposed to just maintenance. The CDC estimates those increased costs to employers at $300 billion a year.

Despite the rising cost of prescription medicines in the US, some suggested solutions fall short and offer only limited relief. For instance, in one article reviewed, a pharmacist suggested cutting medicine costs by ordering pills at a higher dose (since differing doses often cost the same) and then using a pill cutter to cut the pills in half to get the proper dose. She also suggested getting prescriptions filled in 90-day increments, since it's often cheaper to buy meds in bulk. Another suggestion she made was to let your doctor know if you are having trouble affording your medications so that he or she can prescribe more affordable medications, since many doctors don't pay attention to costs unless you alert them about it. While these measures may give a small financial relief, they are really Band-Aids being applied to a much deeper problem. They don't address the underlying problem of high prescription costs inherent in the prevailing prescription drug delivery system.

Who's to blame?

Much of the problem with prescription drug costs might stem from the rise of pharmacy benefit managers, or PBMs. PBMs are companies that manage prescription drug benefits on behalf of health insurers, drug plans, and other payers, including large companies. Originally contracted by insurance carriers to negotiate with pharmaceutical companies, these 'middlemen' have hijacked the prescription drug marketplace to the detriment of pharmacies and patients. For most employee health insurance plans, PBMs act to determine total drug costs for insurers, control access to medications, and determine how much pharmacies are paid. However, PBMs are coming under increasing scrutiny for the role they play, and we feel they shoulder much of the blame for rising drug costs in the US.

Many employee health plans use one of the big three PBMs, Optum, CVS Caremark, and Express Scripts, which control about 85 percent of the marketplace. The problem arises because these giant PBMs cannot serve two masters: they can serve either you, the employer, or their shareholders and board members. After reviewing actual PBM contracts, we found over 72 ways that top PBM contracts force money from your pocket into theirs, many times at your employees' expense and health.

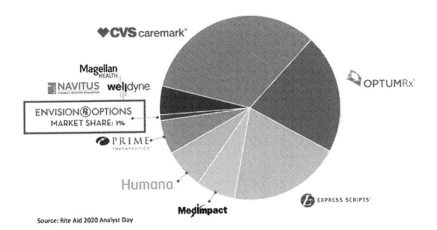

Source: Rite Aid 2020 Analyst Day

Whether by choice or being forced by your health carrier, the prescription drug benefits you can offer using a traditional PBM are limited. You and your employees are likely over-spending on the drugs they do receive, allowing the PBMs to increase their profits at your expense.

Drug manufacturers, health plans and PBMs— an unhealthy alliance

Most pharmacy benefit managers work hand-in-glove with insurance companies to negotiate prices with drug makers. To compete for business, the drug makers often publish high list prices and then offer large discounts or rebates to the PBMs. While those with insurance pay the discounted price, those without insurance are often made to pay the artificially high list price. Thus, drug manufacturers often work together to ensure maximum profitability at the expense of fair pricing. As intermediaries, these companies profit twice on each transaction: They get fees from insurers and employers while obtaining rebates and profit from manufacturers that are hidden from public view. PBMs generate some $315 billion annually from five income streams that include rebate sharing, pharmacy spread, PBM-owned pharmacies, administrative fees, and DIR fees. These monies should be going back to employees and employers, but instead, are adding to the PBMs' profits.

Drug manufacturers, for their part, also offer rebates to PBMs. These rebates allow the PBMs to pay less for the manufacturer's drug, which accomplishes several goals for the manufacturer. These rebates help ensure that their drugs receive preferred placement on the PBM's formulary, which in turn encourages their drug's use over those of their competitors. Thus, when a patient fills a prescription with one of these medications, the drug company pays out a rebate to the PBM. Whether the PBM passes that rebate on to the customer is up to them. BUT MANY DON'T. Research has shown that for every $1 offered as a rebate, the list price increases on average by $1.17. Employers and health insurers are never informed of these rebates and therefore end up paying increased list prices with none of the incentives offered to PBMs.

The second most egregious offense by PBMs happens through something called spread pricing. Most PBMs use what they call the Average Wholesale Price (AWP), which is neither average nor wholesale. Instead, the AWP is an arbitrary price that allows PBMs to inflate drug prices and offer supposed discounts—that aren't really discounts—to health insurers. The PBM keeps the difference between their cost and what they charge the health plan. We also commonly see PBM claw back, when a PBM charges a consumer a copay that is higher than the full cost of the drug and then 'claws back' the extra dollars from the pharmacy.

In addition, many PBMs have alliances with pharmacies and health insurance plans to direct patients to their facilities to purchase drugs to maximize their profits and rebates and to take advantage of spread pricing. Don't believe they are in it for the money? Consider CVS's recent purchase of Caremark for $26.5 billion, followed by Aetna's $69 billion merger with CVS, or Cigna's purchase of Express Scripts for $52 billion. Some PBMs even have PBM 'gag clauses' in their contracts that prevent pharmacists from telling patients when they would pay less for medication by not using insurance. Luckily, around 35 states have already enacted laws in the past decade prohibiting gag clauses, but they do still exist, and it still does happen.

When PBMs call the shots, insurers typically direct their patients toward drug treatments that generate the highest profit margins and the largest rebates. When that happens, patients pay more for drugs and health insurance premiums and receive less effective medical treatments. In the future, this relentless pursuit of rebates could spill over into new markets, including specialty pharmaceutical products and cancer therapies.

Under this nightmare scenario, pharmacy benefit managers would be far worse than costly middlemen. They would control healthcare and pharmaceutical innovation and direct patients toward high profit margins rather than towards high-value care.

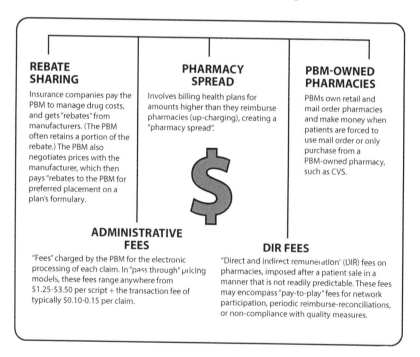

REBATE SHARING

Insurance companies pay the PBM to manage drug costs, and gets "rebates" from manufacturers. (The PBM often retains a portion of the rebate.) The PBM also negotiates prices with the manufacturer, which then pays "rebates to the PBM for preferred placement on a plan's formulary.

PHARMACY SPREAD

Involves billing health plans for amounts higher than they reimburse pharmacies (up-charging), creating a "pharmacy spread".

PBM-OWNED PHARMACIES

PBMs own retail and mail order pharmacies and make money when patients are forced to use mail order or only purchase from a PBM-owned pharmacy, such as CVS.

ADMINISTRATIVE FEES

"Fees" charged by the PBM for the electronic processing of each claim. In "pass through" pricing models, these fees range anywhere from $1.25-$3.50 per script + the transaction fee of typically $0.10-0.15 per claim.

DIR FEES

"Direct and indirect remuneration" (DIR) fees on pharmacies, imposed after a patient sale in a manner that is not readily predictable. These fees may encompass "pay-to-play" fees for network participation, periodic reimburse-reconciliations, or non-compliance with quality measures.

And until you partner with a fiduciary and transparent PBM whose interests align with yours, you put your bottom line at risk, along with your employees' overall health. Because, if an employer wants to give their employees prescription drug benefits that are affordable or even free, they can't do that under *any* of the three big PBMs. The actual number one goal of the largest PBMs is to increase profits, not care for your employees.

Some good news

There is good news. Your company's Rx spend is the most easily impactable cost center. One part of the overall solution is to use a transparent and fiduciary PBM to secure lower prices for medications, which allows employers to pay less for the prescription drug portion of their healthcare plan while giving their employees more benefits at less or no cost.

How do transparent PBMs work?

Transparent PBMs work on pass-through or transparent drug contracts. So, instead of charging arbitrary (and usually inflated) prices to maximize profit, transparent PBMs usually sell prescription drugs at cost and charge only a flat administration fee per prescription filled. Transparent pharmacy benefit managers eliminate DIR fees, PBM owner pharmacies, pharmacy spread, rebate sharing and much more. It is a simple and clear fee-for-service model and a fiduciary partnership.

With this transparent model, employers can see where every dollar of their drug spend goes. In addition, when you work with a PBM that has an aligned interest with you as the employer, they typically pass all rebates and third-party revenue back to you (the employer), further lowering health plan costs. When implementing a transparent PBM, our clients have reduced their overall drug spend anywhere from 40 percent to as much as 72 percent. When you consider that prescription drugs account for nearly a third of a health plan's total spend, that kind of reduction can have a major impact on your overall revenue.

Consider this example from one of our employer clients:

> *Two years ago, we helped the client implement a medical strategy that reduced medical claims costs by almost 40 percent, which lowered the cost of their health plan from eight to five percent of revenue. We next implemented a transparent PBM and saved them 72 percent in the first year, reducing their health plan cost further to only two percent of revenue. As a result of what we implemented, their employees actually got better coverage and lower out-of-pocket costs while the company's profit-sharing amount increased at year's end.*

Other methods can help, too

In addition to implementing transparent PBMs, we also implement patient assistance programs, manufacturer assistance programs, and pharmacy tourism or international sourcing of expensive drugs. All these programs help employees (patients) who must take expensive medications, including brand name and specialty medications. In fact, these medications can make up over half of a company's prescription drug costs even though they may only represent a fraction of the total drugs being prescribed.

Patient assistance and manufacturer assistance programs vary, with some sponsored by a combination of pharmaceutical companies and/or state or local governments and/or not-for-profit organizations. And when we implement purchasing pharmaceuticals internationally, we always make sure to source from industrialized countries with comparable or better standards than the US, like Canada, the UK, or elsewhere.

Regardless of which programs we implement, employers usually see large savings. Here is another recent example of this cost savings strategy in action:

An employee was taking the specialty drug Humira. The employee's monthly dose cost almost $10,000, meaning the employer would have to pay $108,000 annually, and the employee would have to pay $1,000 per month for their portion. Through one of the programs we implemented, we were able to source the drug at no cost for the employee and employer. The employee got their medication for free, and we reduced the employer's annual drug spend by 10 percent.

In the case just mentioned, <u>the employee's cost share of the prescription represented A QUARTER of their $48,000 annual salary</u>. When so many people live paycheck to paycheck, it's easy to understand how many would forgo taking a medication that costs a large portion of their salary. Luckily, with our help, the employer was able to present the employee with an alternative solution that was a win for all involved.

An added bonus: higher employee retention

Naturally, using a transparent PBM along with the other methods discussed, will save employers *and* employees money on prescription drug plans. But the possible benefits go beyond just saving money and ensuring that those insured can get their prescriptions filled.

If companies want to retain their employees, nothing beats a great health plan with a great prescription drug plan. And with their lower pricing and ability to make prescription drugs more available, transparent PBMs can help guarantee the latter. When employees understand and see the benefits of their employer's prescription drug plan, they have a reason to stay, especially since leaving can mean the difference between taking lifesaving or health maintenance drugs or going without. In fact, choosing the right health and drug plan is perhaps too important to burden a typical human resources department with; instead, this important matter should be the task of someone in the C-suite, be they CEO, COO, or CFO.

Protecting your employees

When we look at a typical employer health plan, we see that less than 10 percent of the plan members contribute around 70-80 percent of the plan costs. So as the employer, it makes the most sense to get to know that 10 percent of the population, and work with them to bring the savings by focusing on how they get their medications, where they get them, and what they are getting.

We have already established that the traditional PBM model is focused more on profit than on care. This is apparent when we consistently see employees fill prescriptions for dosages that are too high, brand name drugs that have less efficacy than cheaper options or that serve only to boost PBM profitability, and so on. So, having a PBM partner looking out for your employees' overall well-being is just as important as controlling your overall costs. A true, transparent PBM partner excels at overseeing prescribed medications with clinical rigor. The PBMs we partner with not only have cost controls in place, they also actively manage the prior authorization and clinical due diligence process. While some employees may complain about these prior authorization processes and even feel the PBM may be trying to not give them their medications, they actually exist to ensure cost and quality are not sacrificed in the employee's care, and to verify the patient's diagnosis and recommended drug treatment is correct. Just as a second opinion can prevent unnecessary surgery or an incorrect diagnosis, the second opinion and set of eyes that the prior authorization process provides can confirm that the treatment, drug, and dosages are correct, possibly saving a life.

Next steps

So how do you get started? Your first step is to talk to a benefits consultant who understands the ideas discussed above and the current drug situation in the US. This consultant needs to have access to the types of vendors and solution providers discussed, and they need to know how to do a cost analysis and then implement these programs. When done properly, these programs cause minimal employee disruption or noise and result in almost immediate savings recognized by both the employee and employer. Much like the partnership with a transparent and fiduciary PBM, the broker/consultant's interests must align with the employer's and employees' interests, not with insurer's or the PBM's. In addition, if working with a consultant like us, you may not even have to switch from your current broker to implement the changes we have discussed.

It's your choice, but a simple one

Employers make choices every day that affect the lives of their employees, and none are more important than the health plans and associated prescription drug plans they choose. Many employers, feeling that they have no other viable financial choice, opt for plans connected to the big PBMs, and by doing so they cause their employees to pay more than they should for their medications, which can put ordinary drugs out of the reach of many employees.

At the same time, prices for life-saving and essential medications will likely continue to rise in the US. Because Alec couldn't afford the $1300/month for his life-preserving insulin, and because he made too much money to be put on medical assistance, he died.

Until employers take control of their pharmacy plan, another situation will arise where an employee can't afford their essential medicine, and an outcome like Alec's will happen again. Had Alec's employer put in place the programs and solutions we just covered; Alec might still be alive today.

As an employer, you have the power to make the right life-or-death decision when it comes to choosing a healthcare plan for your employees.

Choosing the right plan, one that offers prescription drug benefits that work, is a decision that you in the C-Suite must make because its ramifications go far beyond being just another company benefit.

Daniel LaBroad

DAN has built Ovation as a fiduciary employee benefits firm focused on results and outcomes. Ovation always acts in the client's best interests when it comes to their benefits program, rather than serving its own interests or those of the insurance companies. Ovation reduces costs through innovative, long-term strategies and cost/risk controls, with a strong emphasis on client experience through employee education and engagement.

Dan's work has been recognized by the benefits industry for over 15 years. He has repeatedly received the prestigious NAHU *Soaring Eagle Award* for demonstrating exceptional professional knowledge and outstanding client service. Dan has consistently been a student and teacher in his industry and has maintained the high moral and ethical character expected of the industry's top representatives.

For the same reasons, industry publications *BenefitsPRO* and *Employee Benefit Adviser* both have featured Dan's professional insights in their pages, and he attracted the attention of the highly influential *Chief Executive* magazine, which featured Dan and his client in a 2020 article, "The Cure for Healthcare Costs." Because of Dan's expertise and industry leadership, he was also invited by the World Health Care Congress, one of the most prestigious events in healthcare, to serve as faculty at their annual event in Washington, D.C.

Dan's motivation always has remained the same: Help businesses protect and grow their bottom line, while giving their employees access to higher quality healthcare at a fair and reasonable price.

To hear more Ovation's client success stories and strategic solutions, listen and watch **The Ovation Show**. Available on YouTube, Spotify, Apple Podcasts, Goodpods, iHeart Radio, C-Suite Radio and more.

CONTACT INFO ───────────────────────────

Connect with Dan on LinkedIn at: https://www.linkedin.com/in/dlabroad/
Email him at: daniel@ovationlife.com | www.ovationlife.com

19

Modern, Mindful Healthcare in a Meta-Hybrid Workforce Culture

by Naama O. Pozniak

N MID-NOVEMBER 2019, JUST MONTHS before the world went into lockdown, I participated in my last Sages & Scientists symposium at Crystal Bridges Museum of Art in Bentonville, Arkansas. Alice Walton, the Walmart heiress, thought-leader, meditator, and philanthropist, hosted the event in her own backyard in the home where she grew up. Under the umbrella of the Chopra Foundation, Alice was joined by co-host Dr. Deepak Chopra, a visionary leader in meditation and Ayurveda, enthusiastic family man, and board-certified in internal medicine, endocrinology, and metabolism. Deepak is the author of more than 90 books, including, *Metahuman: Unleashing Your Infinite Potential*, which had just been published, and was the theme for this unique, collaborative, underground event.

For more than thirty years, as an expert delivering healthcare benefits in our exorbitantly costly, impractical, and frankly broken U.S. healthcare system, I have seen a growing disconnect between leadership and health. This healthcare crisis led me to take responsibility to learn and reimagine how to regain control of our health and influence leaders to rethink their approach.

That fall was busier than ever with traveling, teaching, and leading meditation practice in corporate boardrooms, meetings, and conferences. My team and I were now in the middle of Open Enrollment and delivering the 2020 health insurance benefits packages to our clients. In the middle of my packed schedule, I immediately accepted the last- minute invitation from Crystal Bridges and the Chopra Foundation. So I settled in for three days to participate in a radical reframing of health and well-being's future.

Over the years, I had come to understand that part of helping leaders deliver an improved, attractive, more affordable, and effective way of healing was to bridge Eastern and Western medicine. Merging different modalities creates solutions leaders can leverage, opening new pathways to heal and thrive.

We have all watched healthcare costs spiral out of control, along with the system's confusing premiums and copays and high out-of-pocket expenses. As a result, our employees are growing unhappier, more depressed, and sicker. Not only that, the U.S. delivers the most expensive healthcare system in the world. In 2017, the U.S. spent $3.5 trillion on healthcare, 18 percent of the Gross Domestic Product. In April 2021, one year after the pandemic began, the National Center for Health Statistics reported that 100,000 Americans had died of drug overdoses. You don't need frightening statistics to know that the system and its delivery have taken a devastating toll. The disconnect grows wider across all professions between what leadership can offer our teams and what healthcare means in a holistic framework.

Meta Leadership Is Here

I long ago realized that if leaders bravely open their minds and become willing to engage in mindful meditative practices, collaborate through open communication, embrace technological advances, and provide guidance comprehensively and cohesively, they could transform both themselves and their teams. This Meta way of Leadership would bring fresh, positive energy into a new, hybrid version of healthcare that would liberate people beyond the limitations of health.

Meta leadership was developed by Leonard J. Marcus and Barry Dorn of the National Preparedness Leadership Initiative, or NPI. This method reframes the practice of leadership by providing "a comprehensive organizing framework for understanding and integrating the many facets of leadership and for catalyzing collaborative activity with a focus on improving community functioning and performance." This leadership style will guide reframing what it means to be an expansive, holistic leader with purpose and effort.

I couldn't predict that my three extraordinary days at Crystal Bridges would become a primer on how we, as leaders, could face the pandemic, access care, and transform our mindsets into a Meta Leadership framework. From early morning until late evening, we heard from and met with creative and cutting-edge health and wellness experts, philosophers, artists, technology innovators, spiritual practitioners, physicists, sages, scientists, and AI experts. Those experts included Rudolph E. Tanzi, professor of neurology at Harvard Medical School; Anousheh Ansari, CEO of the XPrize Foundation; Desh Deshpande, chairman of the Sparta Group; Paul Tudor Jones, founder of Tudor Investment; and Dava Newman, Apollo program professor of astronautics at the Massachusetts Institute of Technology, and many more visionaries engaged in a groundbreaking dialogue that explored the frontiers of radical integrative health, humanity, and consciousness.

With focus, innovation, and success, biotechnology was already leading the way in creation of targeted gene therapies for diseases, such as Messenger RNA, to boost the human immune system. But more importantly, under the guidance of some of the world's top experts in Eastern medicine, we could experience ancient, proven techniques to treat and prevent disease. For example, simple meditation techniques and yoga postures immediately brought receptivity and wellbeing to presenters and our audience.

As I sat among my contemporaries in Walton's thoughtfully designed state-of-the-art conference center, I was reminded that every conversation supported and reinforced my vision for adding the Eastern practices of yoga and mindfulness meditation to the new paradigm for delivering healthcare.

The Pandemic's Silver Lining: Mindfulness on a Meta Scale

The scientists and high-tech experts at Crystal Bridges shared technology that would later meet the Covid 19 pandemic on an unimagined scale. But a secondary crisis would soon engulf us. Our healthcare system was not prepared to address our mental and spiritual health's accelerated breakdown beyond the physical pandemic. In June 2021, a Center for Disease Control survey showed that 40 percent of Americans reported mental health issues directly related to the pandemic. It has become clear that the pandemic brought a national crisis on physical, spiritual, and emotional levels into focus.

I have heard the exact words In nearly every conversation with employees, clients, or colleagues at strategy meetings on Zoom or in-person since the pandemic began. "I'm stressed, fearful, and anxious. I'm not eating or sleeping well. I'm barely getting my work done. What can I, or anyone, do?" Nearly every day, I have been asked to lead mindfulness meditation sessions. Every day I share with many leaders at the top of their fields that no matter their profession, position, or skillset, they will benefit on every level when they connect to their breath and health. Once we are in the leadership driver's seat, we should commit to a fundamental, modern way to mix strategies creatively to deliver a mindful way of healing.

We have always been a forward-thinking culture. We face an unpredictable future with unpredictable challenges as part of the reality of rebuilding our teams in a hybrid leadership work environment. When we remain in heightened anxiety, we don't experience the present or recognize solutions right in front of us. From our desks in the c-suite and our home offices, we asked ourselves, how do we re-imagine running our companies We ask ourselves, how do we re-imagine running our companies with a genuinely open mind and heart while delivering the best products and services? How do we provide the most cost-effective, successful healthcare plans to our employees, whose health and mental wellbeing are crucial to our company's culture and long-term success?

There is good news: In a meta culture work environment, where meta means beyond the horizon of what we can see, touch, and feel, we can reframe how we think about wellbeing digitally. Mental health — physical, emotional, and spiritual — has become front and center of every business model. While we're still dealing with security and regulations, we will ultimately protect the clarity and authenticity of health records and leverage technological innovations to maximize an individual's health and wellbeing.

The experts at Crystal Bridges shared examples of technologies that have become part of standard practice today, showing how AI, AR, and VR, can make accurate diagnoses of specific cancers and diseases and how the meta world will help us interact digitally.

Throughout every session and conversation, the topics of mindfulness, meditation, and yoga remained front and center as practical tools to calm our nervous systems, relax and open our hearts, and give us space to re-envision our humanity, our place in our communities, the world, and the cosmos that holds us all.

Western societies require empirical evidence, double-blind trials, and peer-reviewed medical studies to accept and adopt proven healthcare methods from other cultures, such as Ayurveda and Chinese medicine. Yet, evidence shows that stress sends cortisol rushing through our bodies when left unmanaged, which puts us in a perpetual state of flight or fight. A survey conducted in 2017 by the National Institute of Health, NIH demonstrated that cultivating a regular meditation practice decreases our cardiovascular risk, reduces pain, particularly joint pain, improves immune function, increases the production of the anti-aging hormone DHEA, and lowers stress, blood pressure, and cholesterol levels. It is that simple!

So, let me ask this question: Are we too stressed to be blessed and practice mindfulness?

Bringing Mindful Work to Life — Primordial Sound Meditation

As we develop a map for the evolving present, now is the time to move into a mindful meta spaces and intelligently open our hearts, so we are clear, focused, productive and happy. We can start now by taking a long slow, deep breath and feeling relaxed.

There are many techniques we can use to practice mindfulness meditation. However, to experience the rewards, we treat mindfulness like any new skill we learn and implement the methods over time, beginning each day with a simple breath.

Leaders and employers should remember that workers are not robots; we are more than productivity machines. We are mind, body, and spirit. When we fully commit to our practice, we will see that mindfulness leads to happier, healthier engagement, stronger connections, and, yes, increased productivity. In addition, practicing mindfulness will reduce medical expenses overall and the cost of care.

I've been practicing and teaching Primordial Sound Meditation since 2007. Trained with the guidance of Deepak Chopra, there are 108 "seed sounds" that vibrate through the universe. You were born into one of those sounds. Based on your time, date, and place of birth, your mantra allows you to get closer to the sounds of the universe at birth.

Then, like the familiar Om (Ohm), that sound or syllable becomes the word or mantra you use to focus your mind. The mantra becomes valuable when you realize that we have more than 60,000 thoughts per day.

We learn to slow and sometimes even stop our incessant thoughts with simple, daily repetition. Meditation is a lifetime practice. If it was easy, we would call on it the way we call in for a massage appointment, which is why meditation can be challenging, especially in the beginning.

To begin, all you need is 20-30 minutes in a quiet space twice each day. But if you only have five minutes, start there. Techniques like Primordial Sound Meditation tap into the right side of the brain, where creativity and inspiration reside. You will be amazed at how things start to "fall in place"—whether in your work or personal life—as your practice deepens.

Meditation occurs best in a quiet, comfortable space where you will not be distracted. You can also offer a physical or virtual space for teams to come together in a calm area, either for regularly scheduled sessions or just as an escape from the rest of the day. Set a specific time each day for your meditation, move into stillness, and use a timer to help you track your session. Most importantly, breathe!

As we embark on our mindful journeys, remember these "5 Ls":

- Love
- Listen
- Learn
- Laugh
- Let go

Transparency and the Future of Hybrid Health through the Blockchain

In my forthcoming book, *Super Ohmni Leader: An RX for Meta Hybrid Leadership in the New Now*, I share a toolkit for successful leadership. When we put our mindfulness practice in place, we have a vital tool in our kit to help us look beyond our perception of tremendous separation and see that we stand on the threshold of the next evolution in health and wellbeing. Here, mindfulness becomes part of our commitment to heart and spirit, and we have an opportunity to be pioneers and early adopters of Web 3.0

and look beyond broken systems for solutions into the future. For example, non-fungible healthcare will integrate into Web 3.0 information stored in blockchain technology to help eliminate human errors, especially in healthcare where prescription fraud and data theft are now a reality. When we embrace the present innovations creating Web 3.0, we embark upon a collaboration of mind-body-spirit in healthcare leading to:

1. Transparency
2. Authenticity
3. Restoration of data

4. Verification

5. Speed

6. Access

7. Affordability

8. Ownership

9. Unbiased information

10. Interactive community where we can share and access data

In his July 2019 TED Talk, intellectual and historian Yuval Noah Harari says, "The future is about going under your skin and looking directly at what is happening in your heart and your brain. For example, what is your blood pressure, which parts of your brain are activated now? And this can be done with external devices from a ring or a bracelet on your arm, which measure biometric information points. Or there are now devices that, just by looking at your face from a camera, can tell what's happening to your blood pressure or heart rate." Harari adds that along with the latest technological tools, mindfulness powerfully enables us to access the wisdom we have forgotten in our rush toward an imagined "future." With mindfulness in our Meta Leadership tool kit, we will continue to develop the capacity to connect with others with our hearts, minds, and spirit.

Web 3.0 — The Next Generation of Companies — Nonfungible Healthcare.

With new tools in place, we will see an acceleration in the decentralization of our companies' cultures over the next ten years. We'll create solid hybrid communities within our companies to build bridges between the physical and digital worlds — We now call it — The Phygital environment. As we implement these new company structures, we will see much broader adoption of alternative methods of delivering healthcare benefits, including the self-insured model. Coupled with the blockchain, the next generation of leaders will create a revolutionary business model with a renewed focus on community. I predict this more personal and holistic approach will grow a necessary new position: the Mindful Officer, who carries expertise in meditation practice and serves as a connector and a bridge between leaders and employees. With new tools in place, we will see an accelerated decentralization of our companies over the next ten years. And within our companies, we'll create solid hybrid communities that will build bridges between the physical and digital worlds.

The future is the present, and we are living it with the decentralization of healthcare, NFTs, the prioritizing of wellbeing, and the creation of new ways of living culturally so that no single person or group has control over the other. Leaders are already collaborating to bridge the physical world into digitalization and mindfully use the data collected to lead in a transformative way. With mindfulness at the center, we will lead by example and continue to create life-changing technologies and systems in an open- source meta hybrid workplace. This might be the end of this book, but every ending has a new beginning — an endless collaboration and perspective of a shining bright future of health.

We are only at the beginning of the conversation. With our hybrid meta-vision, whether we are fully insured or self-insured, we have the power to shift ourselves mindfully, our families, teams, and communities into health and add compassion and empathy. We can build cultural communities that make a difference, reduce stress, cost and create a positive modern balanced healthcare system that works with every conscious breath.

Namaste

As we enter the new radical leadership future, we are full of creativity, joy and implement a meaningful way of leading communities in the modern meta hybrid culture.

Naama O. Pozniak

Founder/CEO
Rightplan.com

A force within the healthcare and insurance industries, award-winning strategic health insurance advisor Naama O. Pozniak is a mother, lifelong yogi, Primordial Sound Meditation coach, NFT artist, collector, author, and Founder/CEO of Paz Holding, Inc. / RightPlan.com. Naama brings a unique balance of proven mindfulness leadership techniques and corporate wisdom to clients across industries. With the mind of a rock star, the heart of a healer, and the generosity of an avid volunteer, Naama's programs inspire and educate from her 30+ years in the benefits industry and her experiences as a meditation teacher and radical speaker.

As a market disruptor and influencer, Naama is an Associate Publisher and Editorial Board member of Cal Broker magazine, NAHU Region 8 Media Chair, and serves on the LAAHU's board as a HUPAC Chair. In addition, she has led meditation sessions with dozens of organizations over the past 10 years, including Women In Cloud, major insurance carriers, BenefitsPro, ASCEND, and the National Association for Health Underwriters. She brings her wisdom for holistic wellness, leadership, and healthcare costs discussions directly to industry stakeholders in the hybrid meta workforce environment.

Naama teaches timeless techniques proven to help reduce stress and instill a sense of peaceful well-being to family, friends, clients, students, and colleagues. She has developed and led two continuing education courses approved by the Departments of Insurance in California, Florida, Arizona, Nevada, and Texas, showing that implementing an intelligent heart connection and 360-degree care will reduce stress, help us know ourselves better, create happiness, reduce the costs of care, and raise collective awareness.

CONTACT INFO ———————————————————
(818) 508-7177 | naama@rightplan.com | www.rightplan.com

Case Study

Healthcare Costs
Are a Variable Expense

A Case Study from Bart Sheeler,
CEO of Benezon

NOW THAT YOU'VE MADE THE tough decision in the C-suite to manage differently — to stop looking at healthcare as an excise tax and hope it doesn't kill the bottom line — to viewing it as a controllable cost that can be managed, let's make sure you don't lose the momentum. Developing a strategy to save money and looking at healthcare costs as a variable expense just like other supply chains is the first step toward success in reducing healthcare expenses and overall plan costs. Now the focus shifts to implementation and engagement.

Successful implementation will include careful plan design, program promotion, and a year-round focus to utilize the tools and resources to simplify finding care and making good choices.

The key is to promote available programs and services in a continuum that I refer to as **awareness, engagement, and improvement**. The goal here is to first make everybody aware of the programs and services that are available, then help them with engagement—especially with the use of tools and programs throughout the year that will help them with understanding what's possible and making appropriate and sound decisions both for their health, and from a cost-savings perspective. Then as people utilize the resources and tools available they will see improvement in their situation and lower their out-of-pocket cost. Then, as you see engagement across your entire audience, the health plan will see similar reductions in health claims and improved outcomes along the way.

Promote Awareness to Drive Engagement

Let's face it, navigating healthcare can be complex—but your employees don't have to go it alone. To drive engagement, employees first need to be **aware** of the tools and services. Offering and promoting group specific tools and resources that combine intelligent technology with empathetic human support to help guide your employees to **engage** in their health all year long will help you get the most value from the health plan.

Awareness and promotion are a critical first step in familiarizing employees with the tools and resources available. This leads to more informed healthcare decisions and improved outcomes.

- **Multi-Channel Promotion Fosters Program Awareness:** Use a variety of channels to promote the value of the programs and services. This will assure you reach all members in a format that resonates with all employees.

- **Year-Round Communication Drives Member Utilization:** Proactive and predictive outreach using a variety of methods and formats. Program flyers, SMS texts about program tools and resources, even traditional email will communicate program details and raise awareness.

- **Modify and Promote New Plan Design.** You will be making changes to your health plan and how members access health coverage. In your communications, be sure to leverage generic drugs, promote access to telemedicine, and use the available tools and resources. You can even offer to waive deductibles or co-pays when members select lower cost options.

For example: a 1,000-life group in the southeast managed to get over 90 percent engagement from downloading a real-time benefit app, which provided tools and resources that fostered a culture of engagement and participation throughout the year.

Engagement is the Key to a Culture of Savings

We know navigating healthcare can be confusing and often fraught with anxiety at all levels. Health literacy can be a challenge with front-line employees all the way up to the C-suite. Once people are aware of program components, the focus shifts to getting them involved. You may need to proceed with caution and reinforce messaging over and over — empowering them to take responsibility for their own healthcare and learning that engagement is the key to lowering individual and plan costs.

Getting the word out about program changes, new opportunities for cost savings, and highlighting participation incentives will lead to higher engagement rates and create a new *proactive* cultural atmosphere. I refer to this as an alignment of plan design with member utilization that will occur throughout the year.

- **Reduce Anxiety at the Time of Need:** These days, everyone is worried about escalating healthcare costs. Engaging at every step along each employee's health journey will **reduce stress** and tie back to the moment(s) that matter most to each person's unique needs during the year.

- **Combine "High Tech and High Touch" Resources:**
  Offering an array of turnkey tools and relevant program
  information for everyone will optimize member
  engagement and create a rewarding experience that
  promotes a culture of savings for everyone.

- **Human Contact and Hand Holding:** It's often helpful to
  engage a care navigator or advocacy team with appropriate
  support in the time of need.

- **Technology is now a Must Have:** Combining technology
  and benefit apps with the use of toll free number support as
  a self-serve resource to utilize with questions like: "What's
  covered in my plan?" Or, "How can I save on prescription
  drug costs?"

- **In the Moment Support:** Use push notifications and geo-
  fencing reminders to inform members, even before they
  know they need support. This ensures proper use of your
  plan design and leads to better outcomes.

The key is to find the right blend of high-tech and high-touch to
help individuals in the time of need.

Improvement is Improved Culture and Lower Plan Costs

Most executives define savings or return on investment (ROI) in
terms of financial ROI. A few years ago, in looking at service support tickets, it occurred to me that financial ROI is only part of the
equation — which led me to recognize what I now call "Emotional
ROI." This reduces anxiety by solving problems and lowering stress
for plan members. It's not only the financial savings — but the resulting peace-of-mind has as a positive impact on culture and, in
turn, productivity.

Here are a few examples of savings and ROI related to successful
program engagement and utilization.

Financial ROI

- The member's responsibility to date has been adjusted down from $40,714.81 to $8,460.05 — **a savings of over $32,000!**

- Educating the member about available tools, programs and coordination of alternative service options **saved a potential hit on the health plan of $27,000!**

- This service uncovered an Rx cost mark-up of $15,000 on the wholesale cost of a drug priced at $4000. The $19,000 cost was subsequently re-set at the $4000 wholesale rate — **a found savings of $15,000!**

Emotional ROI

- "Thank you for all you've done. You are two angels and your support helped me get through this week."

- "Just used the doctor on the Benefits App. Picked up a prescription a few minutes ago. Saved me from going to the doctor's office and waiting. I'm loving All Savers and the Benefits App."

- "Thank you SO much for all of your hard work and continuous help on this! You did a fantastic job and alleviated a lot of stress from me having to deal with this while pregnant. I cannot thank you enough."

The example below illustrates the importance of year round promotion and encouragement. Don't forget, awareness is the first step to fostering engagement and encouraging participation throughout the year. Skipping natural steps does not work.

A couple years ago, I noticed a group in the Northeast with over 30 locations of similar makeup had three distinct engagement levels. It was interesting to note that after a full year of engagement data for comparison, a third of the groups were enjoying very high engagement, a third were seeing below average engagement, and the remaining third were stuck at the starting gates—yet to even utilize the available tools and services. This speaks directly to the importance of "awareness first", with resource and service promotion directly impacting the downstream engagement rates of members in the various groups. Obviously, if there is poor awareness of available tools, programs, and resources, there will be little to no impact on positive healthcare outcomes or reduced plan costs. Likewise, a successful program can't rely on a couple of announcements at the outset of the plan year. It necessitates year-round promotion and support to become immersed in the culture.

In the end, remember that the goal is to work closely with plan members, service partners, and management to get the message out to employees and increase overall member engagement. By providing hand-holding and guidance, employers will empower individuals to take responsibility for their own health in a manner that eliminates the confusion and anxiety individuals often feel when interacting with the healthcare system.

Show them the new program offers peace-of-mind support and real cost savings. Lower plan costs and overall savings will follow.

Bart Sheeler

CEO & Co-Founder
Benezon | The Benefits App™

Benezon operates a 24/7 cloud-based service business utilizing a white-labeled platform to authorized distribution partners (agencies, brokers and TPAs) as a value added tool and resource for use with their employer groups and employee members—both during open enrollment, and throughout the year. Our services include a technology based app and web portal resources and hands-on concierge advocacy and customer support programs—all dedicated and private labeled to each unique client. Engagement and support are delivered with an industry-leading benefits app, web based member portal and inbound member support via toll free phone, email and chat platforms. We combine numerous resources **all in one place**—connecting members with health plan and benefit information, program details, and additional third party services such as available "no-consult fee" telemedicine designed to offer convenience and yield overall savings to total healthcare costs.

Our focus is on engagement. More importantly, our platform employs technology to help our client partners move their groups along our continuum of success that starts with **creating awareness**, and works through promotion to **drive engagement**—all in an effort to **yield improvement** at both the individual member level and for groups and their self-funded insurance programs.

Our benefits app serves as a hub-and-spoke platform that promotes the right blend of **high-tech** tools and **high-touch** personalized service to foster optimal results. More is available at www.benezon.com.

Your Next Steps . . .

NOW THAT YOU UNDERSTAND CONTINUING with a status quo BUCAH-managed healthcare plan poses an unacceptable risk for your employees and their families, your next step so that you can make the right life and death decision about your healthcare plan is simple:

1) If you received this book from a NextGen Benefits adviser, contact him or her now to schedule a consulting call to discuss your company's healthcare plan options for moving to a quality-first NextGen health plan

OR...

2) If you purchased this book or got it from someone other than a NextGen Benefits adviser, go to the website www.NextGenBenefits.Network to find a NextGen adviser in your area. Contact that adviser today and request a consulting call. (If there is not one nearby, many NextGen advisers work nationally, so contact the one closest to you.)

Congratulations for taking the next step to protect your employees and ensure that they have access to the high-quality, affordable healthcare that you intend for your employees.

And congratulations for leveraging the NextGen Benefits model to make your healthcare a more affordable and sustainable investment that will meet your business objectives.